The Word IN LIFE

PRIORITIES FOR LIVING *Series*

MW00799523

*E*XPERIENCING THE WORD IN YOUR LIFE

➤ *Making God's Word Relevant to Your World Today*

THOMAS NELSON PUBLISHERS
Nashville • Atlanta • London • Vancouver

The Priorities for Living Series:
Experiencing the Word in Your Life

Printed in the United States of America
1 2 3 4 5 — 98 97 96 95 94

Acknowledgments appear on page iv.

Contents

◆ *Acknowledgments* ◆

Chapter 5: The quotes on page 62 are from *More Than Coping* by Elizabeth R. Skoglund (MN: Minneapolis WorldWide Publications, 1987), pp. 52–53. Used by permission.

Chapter 7: The quote on page 84 is taken from "The Idolatry of Politics," *The New Republic* (June 16, 1986), pp. 29–36.

Chapter 11: The story on page 131 is taken from *Against All Hope* by Armando Valladares (New York: Ballantine Books, 1986), pp. 255–258. Used by permission.

Chapter 12: The story on page 148 is taken from *13 Fatal Errors Managers Make* by W. Steven Brown © 1985. Published by Fleming H. Revell Company, a division of Baker Book House. Used by permission.

Unless noted otherwise, stories about persons in this book are fictitious. Any resemblance to actual persons or incidents is coincidental.

Narrative and questions written by Ken Abraham and Dietrich Gruen.

◆ *Foreword* ◆

The *Priorities for Living* series has been created to offer you friendly companions for discovering the relevance of God's Word and for applying it to everyday life. The series addresses a variety of issues that believers face in today's world. It contains a wide selection of articles and relevant Scripture from *The Word In Life Study Bible*™, which allow these workbooks to be used as independent tools for individual or group study. Each workbook in the series is based on a theme that has been developed in *The Word In Life Study Bible*™.

It has been said that Scripture was not written merely to be read, but to change lives. James urges us to be "doers of the word, and not hearers only" (James 1:22). The purpose of God's Word is to help us become more like Jesus Christ by making the Word of God part of our lives. *The Word In Life Study Bible*™ was created to help us discover how to relate God's Word to the world we live in.

Applying biblical truth today is not always easy—especially since the Bible was written thousands of years ago. Many wonder how the Bible can be connected to today's complex society. However, as you explore the pages of this book, you will discover how surprisingly relevant God's Word is to your daily life and how you can make a difference in your world.

WHAT DOES THE BIBLE HAVE TO DO WITH ME?

Tens of millions of adults are rediscovering the Bible and are seeking a deeper relationship with God. A recent poll reported in U.S. News & World Report revealed that "more than 80 percent [of Americans], including 71 percent of college graduates, believe the Bible is the inspired Word of God." In the same poll, 76 percent of the respondents believe that "God is a heavenly father who can be reached by prayers." He is not merely an "idea" or an "impersonal creator."

Yet, questions abound concerning the Bible and God, especially in regard to what it means to be a contemporary Christian in a secular society. Does being a Christian mean you should give up your career and become a monk? Should you donate your designer clothing to the poor and replace them with drab rags? If being a Christian means following Jesus, how can you bridge the two-thousand-year gap between His time and ours? What does it mean to be like Jesus today?

Perhaps you have asked some of these questions:
- Is God real?
- What is the gospel, anyway?
- What does it really mean to have a relationship with Christ?
- How does my relationship with Jesus impact upon my attitudes and actions at work?
- How can I find forgiveness for things in my past?
- How can I share my faith without making people mad at me?
- What does it really mean to repent and change my ways?
- How can I love people when I don't even like them?

These are just a few of the questions we will explore in this workbook. As we do, we will search for practical answers. We will attempt to move out of the realm of theory, and enter real life to find usable applications of biblical principles. We will experience the Word of God in our lives and discover fresh ways of making His Word relevant to our world.

Obviously, in a book this size we won't be able to answer every question you have about the Bible and God. It will, however, provide a good overview of the Christian faith. Other books in this series are designed to further examine particular aspects of the Christian life, and you will benefit greatly by studying these topics.

Who Will Benefit from This Workbook?

Whether you are new to Christianity or you're a longtime believer, you probably have wondered what the Bible has to do with your life today. After all, the Bible was written a long time ago.

One of the most amazing things about the Bible is that its principles are just as relevant today as they were when they were written. This workbook is designed to help you discover how to put these principles to work in your life. Some of the principles that are presented will be reminders of values you learned long ago; others will offer new insights for applying God's Word to your daily life.

Christ calls you to take His Word into your world and to live out your life with such honesty, integrity, and transparency that everyone around you can see God working in and through you. In Matthew 10:25, Jesus says that "it is enough for a disciple that he be like his teacher, and a servant like his master."

For early believers, being like Jesus meant they would face persecution and martyrdom. But what else does it mean to "be like Jesus," especially for Christians in today's world? Matthew gives us some clues throughout his account of Jesus' life on earth.

To be like Jesus means we need to:
- Accept our roots
- Engage the world's pain and struggle
- Commit ourselves to other believers
- Admit our vulnerability to temptation
- Openly proclaim the message of Christ
- Commit ourselves to changed thinking and behavior
- Serve others, especially those who are oppressed or without Christ
- Affirm others in leadership

We will explore each of these points throughout the workbook. When you commit yourself to following Christ, you open yourself to the wonderful future He has in store for you.

How to Use This Book

This workbook is designed to help you live out your walk with Christ in the world. Although the book is directed to you, the individual reader, and is primarily intended as a private volume in which you can record your personal responses, it can also be used as a group study and discussion guide. If the workbook is used for group study, each member of the group should have his or her own book to ensure privacy. A Leader's Guide is included in the back of this workbook.

Each lesson is self-contained and is made up of thought-provoking articles, relevant Scripture, and practical applications. To gain the maximum benefit from your workbook, please read all of the material in each chapter. Throughout the book, you will be invited to write your responses to specific questions based upon what you have read. Many of your responses will involve your personal thoughts, feelings, experiences, and areas of your life in which you sense the need to improve.

Obviously, you could answer the questions mentally and then move on to the next subject, but it is extremely helpful to put your answers on paper. As you record your responses, you will begin to think through why you feel and believe the way you do. More important, you will have a written record of some matters about which God may be speaking to you concerning your attitudes and actions.

When you write your responses, express your thoughts and feelings as freely and honestly as possible. Don't worry about spelling, grammar, or sentence structure. Don't try to impress anyone with your answers. No teacher or critic is looking over your shoulder, waiting to correct you if you record the wrong response. In fact, most of your responses cannot be considered right or wrong since they are simply reflections of your own thoughts and feelings. No tests will be given at the end of the book; it's a course you're sure to pass with flying colors!

When using your workbook, find a quiet, comfortable place where you can be free to express your thoughts and feelings without interruption. Allow yourself plenty of time to read each chapter carefully, then thoughtfully respond to the questions. Seek the Lord's guidance concerning areas in which He may want you to change.

Remember, you may not be able to change many of the circumstances in your life. But you can change your own attitudes and actions, and that will make your time with this workbook a rich and worthwhile experience. Happy working!

GETTING THE BIG PICTURE

*T*he television cameras were rolling when the front doors to First Church opened at the conclusion of the Sunday morning service and members of the congregation began scurrying through the exit. The local television news team was doing a series of reports on fading religion as the world prepares to step into the twenty-first century. This week's report would feature Christians from First Church. Most of the members attempted to avoid the raft of microphones, cameras, and lighting equipment, except for Brother Bob. His imposing physique filled the doorway, blocking the path of the exiting worshipers behind him.

"Do you regularly attend services at First Church?" a reporter asked.

"Yes, of course I do," Brother Bob replied with a self-righteous sniff.

"And are you a Christian, Sir?"

"I sure am!"

"If you don't mind, Sir, what does it mean to be a Christian?"

"Well, Son, it means that I believe in God and trust Jesus for my salvation."

Feeling like he had answered enough questions for the day, Brother Bob started down the steps. But the reporter, undaunted by Brother Bob's attempt to finish the interview, followed Bob and said, "Excuse me again, Sir. I've read that Jesus said a Christian should love God with all his heart, soul, mind, and strength. And a Christian is supposed to love his neighbor as himself. Tell us, Sir, do you really love God with *all* your heart?"

"Of course. Well, I mean, I guess so."

"And all your soul and mind? *All*?"

"Well, you know, I'm a busy person. I can't be thinking about God *all* the time. I'm only human, you know."

"What about your neighbor? Do you love your neighbor as yourself? I'd think that would be hard."

"You'll have to excuse me now, young man. I think I hear my wife calling. Sure has been nice talking to you . . ."

◆ ◆ ◆ ◆ ◆ ◆ ◆ ◆ ◆

Maybe you can identify with Brother Bob's comment. You do love God, but do you love Him with all your heart? Honestly, now. Do you love God with all your soul, mind, and strength? Most of us aren't even sure what that means!

If you find your answer a bit perplexing, you are not alone. Many of us are so busy with work, school, and family responsibilities, our schedules don't seem to leave much time for loving God. Yet, Jesus isn't interested in recruiting "weekend warriors"—Christians who want to serve Him for one or two hours each week in church and then live the rest of the week for themselves. Nor does He appreciate the token "tips" of our time, money, and resources we sometimes try to toss to Him in lieu of our total commitment. To be a Christian doesn't mean that you give Jesus 50 percent of your life, or even 95 percent. To be a follower of Jesus, you must give Him all of your life and serve Him in all that you do and all that you have.

LIFE—THE BIG PICTURE

When Jesus recited the greatest of the commandments (Mark 12:29–30), He repeated the word "all" four times. What aspects of life was He including? *Later, Paul emphasized that "all things were created" through and for Christ (Col. 1:15–18, emphasis added). How much of "all" is all?*

Here's how a typical American who lives to be 75 years old will have spent life:

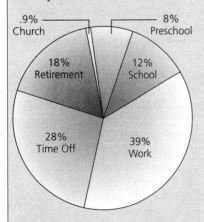

.9% Church — 8% Preschool — 18% Retirement — 12% School — 28% Time Off — 39% Work

In light of this use of time, when does a person "love the Lord God" as Jesus commanded? Is that limited to what one does for an hour or so on Sunday morning? If so, then worship takes up a mere 3,900 hours, or 0.9 percent, of one's waking life—assuming that one goes to church *every* Sunday for 75 years!

Is that what Jesus or Paul had in mind? No, Christ is Lord of *all* of life—not just Sunday mornings, but weekdays, too, including time at work. Further-

more, He is Lord not only of our time, but of our money and possessions as well. Unfortunately, many Christians in the West have developed some dangerous attitudes in these areas that push God to the fringes of life. For example:

Myth: One-seventh of our time belongs to God. Some Christians speak of Sunday as "the Lord's day," a day for religion. And so it might be if Christians worshiped from sunup to sundown. But for most people Sunday worship means an hour-long service before an afternoon of televised sporting events. Thus the "day of worship" is effectively reduced to less than one-twentieth of the week.

That was never what God intended. Originally, the seventh day or Sabbath rest was viewed as the completion of the week, not a break or separation from the work week. It was a time for review, celebration, and restoration.

Yet already by Jesus' day there were major distortions regarding the Sabbath. It had become a day of legalistic ritual. Jesus

sought to restore it as a day of compassion and worship (Luke 6:1–11; John 5:1–18).

Dedicating *all* of our time to God does not mean apportioning so much to family, so much to a job, so much for ourselves, and a little left over for God. No, all 168 hours of the week, all 52 weeks of the year, and all of the years of a lifetime belong to God and are on loan to us to manage for Him.

Myth: Ten percent of our money belongs to God. Some Christians believe that God expects them to give a flat 10 percent of their income to church and other ministries. The reality is that on the average, American believers give only 2.3 percent of their income to religious or charitable causes of any kind.

The underlying principle that needs to be considered is that God has given us the ability to earn money, so actually all 100 percent of our earnings belong to Him. We are called to manage our money—not just what we give away, but what we keep, too—according to His values. Tithing was intended as a discipline to remind God's people that all of what they have or earn belongs to Him. Originally a voluntary activity (Gen. 14:13–24; 28:20–22), it was intended for the care of others and as a representation of the worship of God (Deut. 26:1–19).
continued

continued

Tithing was never intended to replace obedience to *all* of God's commands (Matt. 23:23–24).

Myth: Only some real estate belongs to God. Too many Christians have fallen into a dangerous pattern of identifying a few buildings as the Lord's property—religious institutions like churches, schools, and church-owned hospitals. By implication, other real estate is ours to do with as we please.

However, Scripture opposes that view. Paul says that "all things were created through Him and for Him" (Col. 1:16). Even our bodies are "temples of God" (1 Cor. 6:19). God calls us to serve Him in *all* that we do (Col. 3:17). Therein lies the path to true blessing, peace, and truth. Christ has come to break our bondage to anything less. Equipped by His Spirit within us and instructed by His written Word, we can live *wholly* for the kingdom. ◆

 Mark 12:28–34

[28]Then one of the scribes came, and having heard them reasoning together, perceiving that He had answered them well, asked Him, "Which is the first commandment of all?"

[29]Jesus answered him, "The first of all the commandments *is:* 'Hear, O Israel, the LORD our God, the LORD is one. [30]And you shall love the LORD your God with all your heart, with all your soul, with all your mind, and with all your strength.' This *is* the first commandment. [31]And the second, like *it, is* this: 'You shall love your neighbor as yourself.' There is no other commandment greater than these."

[32]So the scribe said to Him, "Well *said,* Teacher. You have spoken the truth, for there is one God, and there is no other but He. [33]And to love Him with all the heart, with all the understanding, with all the soul, and with all the strength, and to love one's neighbor as oneself, is more than all the whole burnt offerings and sacrifices."

[34]Now when Jesus saw that he answered wisely, He said to him, "You are not far from the kingdom of God."

But after that no one dared question Him.

---

1. Look again at the pie chart on page 2 that shows how the typical American spends life. What surprises you the most about these statistics?

_____

_____

2. Think of activities during an average week; how much time do you spend on:

_____ %	physical exercise	_____ %	spiritual activities
_____ %	intellectual pursuits	_____ %	activities with my family
_____ %	community service	_____ %	watching television
_____ %	sleeping	_____ %	work

3. What surprises you the most when you review how you spend your time? In what areas do you feel you should be spending less time? more time?

_____

_____

4. Jesus told the man who had posed the question concerning the greatest of the commandments that he was not far from the kingdom of God. What did Jesus mean?

_____

_____

_____

——◆ The Price of Love ◆——

When you hear the word gospel, *you may recall that the word means "good news." But have you ever stopped to consider what the gospel really is? Simply put, the essence of the gospel is that Christ died for us while we were still sinners. Jesus willingly came into the world to show us how to live, and then to pay the price for our sins. He loved every one of us enough to die an excruciating death for our sins. Why would He do it? Maybe this story will help you understand better.*

◆ ◆ ◆ ◆ ◆ ◆ ◆ ◆ ◆

Before the transplanting of human organs became commonplace, a young boy developed a deadly kidney infection. Doctors worked around-the-clock in their attempt to save the boy, but all of their efforts produced nothing but failure. The boy's kidneys were so diseased that they could not possibly purify his system. There seemed to be no hope; the boy's parents could only stand by helplessly and watch their son die.

In desperation, one of the doctors made a suggestion to the dejected parents. "It's never been done before," he said hesitantly, "but if we can find a person whose blood type is the same as your son's, maybe— just maybe—we could run your son's blood through the system of the healthy person. Perhaps the kidneys of the healthy person could do the work that the boy's system cannot do. There is great risk involved here, for your son as well as the donor," warned the doctor.

The parents looked hopefully at each other and nodded. "It's our only chance, Doctor," the father answered. "Let's do it."

"All right, we must hurry. Does anyone here have the same blood type as the boy?"

"I do," said the dad.

"And you are willing to volunteer?" the doctor asked, the concern evident in the tone of his voice.

"I am," responded the father. "Let's get on with it."

Quickly the medical staff tested the father's blood to make certain it was the same type as the boy's. They prepped the father, wheeled his gurney into the operating room, parked it beside his son's, and went to work. They tenuously arranged tubing from the father to the son and back again, so the father's system could purify the boy's blood. After a while, both the father and the son were out of critical danger and the operation was hailed a huge success.

Seven days later the boy was released from the hospital, along with his father. The family was reunited for only two days when the father's temperature suddenly skyrocketed and, almost immediately, the father died.

The boy lived, but at the cost of his dad's life. His father had taken upon himself the sickness, fever, disease, and death that had belonged to his child. Only one thing motivates a person to make such an extreme sacrifice—love. ◆

WHAT IS THE GOSPEL?

Fewer and fewer people today understand the meaning and significance of the term *"gospel."* To many it is little more than a category of the music industry—songs with simple melodies and harmonies that honor traditional themes and religious devotion. Yet Jesus told John's followers that one way they could tell He was the Messiah was that because of His coming, *"the poor have the* gospel *preached to them" (Luke 7:22, emphasis added).*

What is the gospel, and why was it significant for Jesus to preach it? The Greek word translated *gospel* can mean either "a reward for bringing good news" or simply "good news." From the standpoint of the New Testament, the ultimate good news is that Jesus Christ has come as the Messiah, the Savior of the world. He has come to save people from sin and restore them to God.

The Good News

That is indeed good news because it speaks to the very bad news that apart from God's intervention, all the world would be lost and without hope. As Paul declared in Romans, his monumental work explaining the gospel, "All have sinned and fall short of the glory of God" (Rom. 3:23). The good news is that "while we were still sinners, Christ died for us" (5:8). Indeed, Christ's death, which dealt with sin, and His resurrection from the dead form the core of the gospel message and ground that message in historical events (1 Cor. 15:1–4).

Obviously, though, Jesus had not yet gone to the cross at the time John's followers came, asking whether He was the Christ. Nevertheless, His message of the kingdom was good news because it revealed that God was finally bringing about the salvation promised in the Old Testament. Jesus' coming was like a fireman arriving on the scene of a fire or an emergency medical team arriving at an accident. The situation was not yet remedied, but the remedy was at hand. That was good news!

The Gospel for the Poor

But Jesus said it was especially good news for the poor (Luke 7:22). He had told the hometown crowd at Nazareth the same thing, that He had come "to preach the gospel to the poor" (Luke 4:18). Likewise, in the Sermon on the Mount He taught, "Blessed are you poor, for yours is the kingdom of God" (Luke 6:20). In what sense

continued

continued

was Jesus' message of the kingdom particularly for the poor?

You might say Jesus was announcing an "upside-down kingdom." Whereas the kingdoms of the world are set up by and for the powerful and the advantaged, His kingdom was offered to the destitute, the wretched, the broken, and the hopeless, to those stripped of their dignity and self-respect. The "poor in spirit" were not merely the humble, but the humiliated, those who have had their spirits crushed and are knocked down by circumstances.

The poor were easy to spot in Jesus' day. They included widows and orphans, slaves and prisoners, the sick and demon-possessed, the homeless and the hungry. In our own day we could add people grieving the loss of a loved one or the end of a marriage, those who have lost jobs, or those who have been victimized by crime or injustice.

To these Jesus preached good news. He invited them to become part of a new family, a new community, the church. The rich are invited as well, but as in the parable of the slighted invitation, most reject the offer, feeling sufficient in themselves to take care of their needs.

But those who accept Jesus' invitation do so by believing in His work on the cross on their behalf. That involves more than mere intellectual agreement to a theoretical truth. It means admitting their sinful condition and placing trust in Jesus to deal with their sin. It means entering into a vital relationship with the living Christ Himself.

The Purpose of the Gospel

When people believe, Christ begins to fashion them into a community of faith, the body of Christ (Eph. 2:1—3:11; 1 Pet. 2:9–10). His ultimate purpose in the gospel is to create a new people who live out the message, relationships, and values of His kingdom, a kingdom in which justice replaces injustice, community replaces rugged individualism, and compassion reigns over competition and neglect of others.

Thus the gospel is not merely a private relationship with God, but a public expression of godliness as well. The good news about Jesus certainly affects one's personal life, transforming individual attitudes and habits. But it challenges us to look beyond our own self-interests to the interests of others, both those in our network of relationships and in the world in general (Rom. 12:3–8; Eph. 4:1–16; Phil. 2:1–11). To embrace the gospel is to live no longer for oneself, but to live for Christ.

Spreading the Gospel

Moreover, Christ has commissioned His followers to spread the good news about Him throughout the world. This involves both the verbal proclamation of gospel truth and the demonstration of gospel reality in the lives of believers. Both can happen in a variety of ways: through preaching and teaching, through Christian worship and daily disciplines of spiritual life, through works of mercy and programs of compassion that meet basic human needs, or through believers taking moral stands.

The Four Gospels

During the second century, the term "gospel" came to mean the authoritative message about Jesus that the apostles had left and especially the four written accounts of His life and teaching, Matthew, Mark, Luke, and John. Mark was probably the first to be written, but all were created to be more than mere biographies about an historical figure. Each portrays the Lord in a particular way to show His saving significance for all people and to call them to respond in faith to His good news. ◆

THE GOOD NEWS

WHILE WE WERE STILL SINNERS CHRIST DIED FOR US . . . .

Luke 7:22–23

²²Jesus answered and said to them, "Go and tell John the things you have seen and heard: that *the* blind see, *the* lame walk, *the* lepers are cleansed, *the* deaf hear, *the* dead are raised, *the* poor have the gospel preached to them. ²³And blessed is *he* who is not offended because of Me."

1. Many people have misconceptions about what the gospel is and what it means to be a Christian. Which of the following misconceptions about Christianity have you or a friend ever held?

Living out the gospel and being a Christian means:

_____ Going to church, especially at Christmas and Easter.
_____ Giving money to the poor.
_____ Being a "good" person.
_____ Not drinking, smoking, or carousing.
_____ Knowing that God is love; therefore He will not punish anyone.
_____ Knowing that God is the Boss.

2. According to the article on page 5, what is the "bad news" of the gospel?

_____

_____

_____

3. How does your understanding of the bad news affect your appreciation of the "good news"?

_____

_____

_____

4. List some ways your personal relationship with Christ should impact your public conduct.

_____

_____

_____

_____

_____

◆ The Bible Is No Ordinary Book! ◆

The next time you're in a bookstore, wander over to the self-help section. Browse through the titles, and you will be amazed at the large number of books offering guidance for living a better life. Do you need a crash course in how to be more productive? There's a book for it. Need to learn how to cope with daily stresses? There's a book for it. Or, maybe you would like to know how you can improve your family relationships. You will probably find an entire section on that subject!

Yet, despite all these guides for improving certain aspects of life, only one book gives us guidance for every aspect of our lives—the Bible. God knew that we would need help getting along in this crazy and sometimes frustrating world. That's why He inspired men to record His advice in the Bible.

While skeptics attempt to lump the Bible alongside other religious books, a brief overview of the Bible quickly reveals its uniqueness. The Bible was written over a period of nearly two thousand years, by forty authors from various walks of life, and in three languages (Hebrew, Greek, and Aramaic). Although the majority of the Bible's writers never met, they present a unified picture of God, a central message of Jesus Christ as God coming to earth as man, and they address some of the most controversial topics of their time (and ours!) without contradicting one another.

Amazing? It certainly is. God has given us this special book to communicate His personal message in a way we can easily understand. In the pages of the Bible you will discover who God is, how you can get to know Him personally, and how you will benefit from living your life according to God's principles.

The Bible also provides an objective, trustworthy standard of truth—not the world's perception of truth, but God's absolute truth. In a world that can't make up its mind about right and wrong, the Bible stands as a perfect measuring stick against which every thought, word, and deed can be evaluated.

THE BIBLE: GETTING THE BIG PICTURE

As Paul indicates to Timothy (2 Tim. 3:16–17) *and many other passages affirm, the Bible is the ultimate authority for Christian faith and practice. It is crucial to interpret Scripture in light of its overall context.*

The Bible as it has come down to us is laid out in two parts: the Old Testament, covering the period before Christ, and the New Testament, the period after Christ. The biblical record is a three-part story.

Part I: God's Original Creation (Gen. 1–2)

The eternal God created a perfect, beautiful world and put it under the management of Adam and Eve and their successors (Gen. 1–2). No one knows how long this part of the story lasted, but Scripture devotes only the first two of its 1,189 chapters to telling it.

continued

continued

Part II: The Human Dilemma and God's Response (Gen. 3—Rev. 20)

The second part of the story takes up all but the last two chapters of the Bible. Two story lines weave throughout the record. One reveals how the balance and beauty of creation is terribly damaged by sin and rebellion. The other unfolds God's response to rescue His creatures and the creation from this dilemma. His redemptive work is promised through Israel (as recorded in the Old Testament), provided through Christ (as recorded in the gospels), and then applied in and through the church (as told in Acts and the letters). The book of Revelation's first 20 chapters display events related to Christ's return to earth.

Part III: The Achievement of God's Original Design (Rev. 21–22)

The last two chapters of the Bible tell the final third of the story. They offer great hope to the reader by promising a new heaven and earth. God's original intentions for the creation will finally and fully be achieved. This parallels and fulfills Genesis 1–2 and also reflects the values of Christ, who is the focus of the whole Bible.

Reading the Bible

Because the middle third of the account comprises 99 percent of the text, it grabs most of the attention of Bible readers. But to properly understand it, one must keep the first and third parts firmly in mind. Like two bookends, they frame and anchor the big picture of God's work throughout history. They provide the crucial context for the double story line of rebellion and restoration etched through the middle of the account.

That middle part often makes for rather painful reading. With forceful realism it shows the cruelty that sin unleashes on all of creation. Some readers would prefer to skip over or dismiss that aspect of the story. But God refuses to distort reality or put a positive "spin" on it. He includes the horrors of sin in His record as "examples to avoid" (1 Cor. 10:6). He lets nothing escape either exposure or resolution in Jesus Christ. ◆

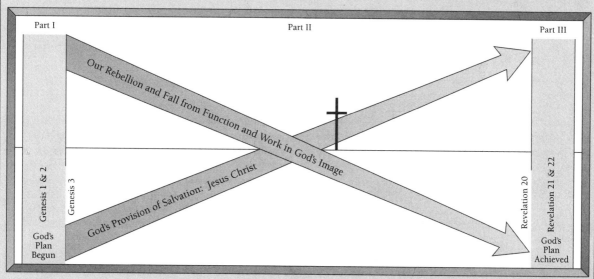

Part I

Part II

Part III

Our Rebellion and Fall from Function and Work in God's Image

God's Provision of Salvation: Jesus Christ

Genesis 1 & 2

Genesis 3

God's Plan Begun

Revelation 20

Revelation 21 & 22

God's Plan Achieved

CREATION, REBELLION, AND RESTORATION

2 Timothy 3:16–17

¹⁶All Scripture *is* given by inspiration of God, and *is* profitable for doctrine, for reproof, for correction, for instruction in righteousness, ¹⁷that the man of God may be complete, thoroughly equipped for every good work.

1. Some specialty publications claim to be "The Bible" for their particular field, such as "The Baseball Bible" or "The Bible of Marketing." What book is "The Bible" in your business or hobby?

_____

_____

2. List some things that make the Bible different from any other book.

_____

_____

_____

3. What would you say to someone who asked you, "How do you know you can trust the Bible? Isn't it full of errors and contradictions?"

_____

_____

_____

_____

4. In 2 Timothy 3:16–17, Paul says that all Scripture is *inspired* (the word literally means "God-breathed"). That doesn't mean that God handwrote the Bible, but He did inspire select believers to write His Word so we could all have access to it. Although the writers wrote out of their own historical and cultural contexts, they wrote what God instructed them to write. How does the knowledge that God inspired the Scriptures affect your willingness to trust the Bible as your guide to life? Check all that apply.

_____ I believe the Bible and use its teachings as my guide.
_____ The Bible is merely a collection of myths and moral stories.
_____ The Bible is the standard by which I judge between right and wrong.
_____ The Bible is interesting reading, but I don't live my life by it.
_____ I read the Bible regularly and trust it to be the absolute authority in my faith and life.

◆ Should Christians Just Give Up? ◆

"Mary, did you see that item on the news last night about all the gangs that are vandalizing our neighborhoods?" Josie asked.

"No, I don't watch the news anymore," Mary answered. "It's too depressing. All you hear about are murders, rapes, gang violence, government frauds, and rip-offs. Who needs it? I'd rather just keep the TV turned off."

"But Mary," Josie protested, "if we don't know what's going on in the world, how are we ever going to make a difference?"

"Oh, Josie, wake up! It seems like nothing we do to try to get rid of all the problems makes a difference. Violence just keeps spreading. What's the use?"

"Well, if we don't keep trying to reach out to others, then who will?" ◆

FAITH IMPACTS THE WORLD

Jesus sent His followers into "all the world" (Mark 16:15). Clearly He had global impact in mind. But spreading Christ's message involves more than just broadcasting a statement or set of facts. How does faith *impact* the world?

One way is through followers of Christ who live out the gospel and proclaim it to the world. That's why the lifestyles and relationships of believers are so important. People are watching to see how we as Christians handle our responsibilities and resources. Is there any evidence that Christ really makes a difference in our lives?

Another way is through Christian institutions, such as local churches, parachurch organizations, and the Christian media. If you work or volunteer for one of these kinds of organizations, you have an important opportunity to touch the needs of the world with Christ's love and power.

A third sphere of influence is through lobbying and advocacy. Here Christians attempt to influence the institutions and people that control society. This might mean something as simple as voting, or something as complex as running for office or working to enact a particular piece of legislation. In our culture, Christians have the right to participate actively in public policy decisions, and we should use that right in ways that we believe honor the Lord.

As we attempt to take Christ's message to "all the world," it helps to understand how our world operates.

Mark 16:14–20

[14]Later He appeared to the eleven as they sat at the table; and He rebuked their unbelief and hardness of heart, because they did not believe those who had seen Him after He had risen. [15]And He said to them, "Go into all the world and preach the gospel to every creature. [16]He who believes and is baptized will be saved; but he who does not believe will be condemned. [17]And these signs will follow those who believe: In My name they will cast out demons; they will speak with new tongues; [18]they will take up serpents; and if they drink anything deadly, it will by no means hurt them; they will lay hands on the sick, and they will recover."

[19]So then, after the Lord had spoken to them, He was received up into heaven, and sat down at the right hand of God. [20]And they went out and preached everywhere, the Lord working with *them* and confirming the word through the accompanying signs. Amen.

. . . Christ came, who is over all,
the eternally blessed God. Amen.
—*Romans 9:5*

FAITH IMPACTS THE WORLD

GOVERNMENT

BUSINESS

SERVICE

WORKPLACE

COMMUNITIES

FAMILIES

Policies

Laws

Values

Beliefs

Traditions

1. How does Jesus' command to go into all the world, telling everyone the good news, affect your concept of the Christian life?

_____ It scares me.
_____ It depresses me because I'm not the evangelist or missionary type.
_____ It challenges me to get involved in the world where people need to hear about Christ.

2. What are some practical ways your faith in Christ can impact your world?

_____

_____

_____

3. List some ways you can be involved in taking the gospel to the world through your church.

_____

_____

_____

_____

◆ ◆ ◆ ◆ ◆ ◆ ◆ ◆ ◆

Being a Christian does not mean "parking your brains" outside the church doors before entering. Nor does it mean hiding your head in the sand when you leave the church. God calls us to love Him with our whole hearts, and then share His love with the whole world. He has given us His Word, the Bible, and the gospel of Jesus so we might have life and so we can share His message with others.

Before we can truly spread the word about Christ's love and hope with anyone else, however, we must be convinced of it ourselves. In our next chapter, we'll explore what it really means to be followers of Jesus and why it is so important that our friends and family members find out about Him, too.

UNFOLDING FAITH

Thanks to modern technology, we live in an "instant society." Things that used to take hours or even days to complete can now be done in minutes. For example, fax machines transmit documents thousands of miles in a matter of seconds, while satellites beam television pictures of events happening around the world into our living rooms.

Meals that used to take hours to prepare can be made in half the time in a microwave oven. Still, we are impatient. We put a two-minute pastry in the microwave and then start pacing. What's taking so long? we wonder.

This penchant for instant gratification even spills over into our spiritual lives. Some people assume that once they have trusted Christ as their Savior they have secured their passage to heaven, so they can get on with the rest of life here on earth. They act as though being a Christian is something that happens once and zap! That's it.

But there is no such thing as an "Instant Christian." Yes, you become a Christian when you commit your life to Christ, but being a Christian and living a Christlike lifestyle require growth and maturation—and that takes time.

FAITH UNFOLDS SLOWLY

How much do you understand about the faith? Do you wish you knew more? Perhaps others intimidate you with their knowledge and familiarity with Scripture.

If so, Jesus' work with His disciples (Mark 4:33–34) can lend some helpful perspective. Just as our biological lives unfold slowly, so do our spiritual lives. God offers us what we can understand as soon as we can handle it, but not before. Most parents would consider explicit lessons on sexuality to be premature for preschoolers. Likewise, driving lessons for first graders would be inappropriate. And some athletic activities can cause great dam-age if children engage in them too early in their development. In the same way, God holds back certain lessons until we're mature enough to handle them.

Jesus called the disciples to follow Him one day at a time (Luke 9:23). But He also promised them that the Spirit would come later and lead them into truths that they could not handle then (John 16:12–16). Like those first disciples, we as Jesus' modern-day followers are not to know the end from the beginning, but to learn something from Him every day, applying it to our lives. Faith is not a badge to be worn or knowledge to be flaunted, but a little seed to be nurtured (Mark 4:26–32).

Mark 4:33–34

³³And with many such parables He spoke the word to them as they were able to hear *it*. ³⁴But without a parable He did not speak to them. And when they were alone, He explained all things to His disciples.

1. Why do you think Jesus spoke to the crowds in parables? Check all that apply.

_____ To confuse His listeners
_____ To challenge His listeners to think about the deeper meaning of His words
_____ To baffle His enemies
_____ To present truth in such a way that even the common people, who were untrained in theology, could understand

2. How do you think Jesus' explanation of His parables to His disciples might differ from the message Jesus presented to the multitudes?

_____

_____

_____

3. Check all the statements below which reflect your understanding, acceptance, and application of the gospel in your life.

_____ I'm fairly sure I understand the gospel, but I can't really explain it to someone else.
_____ I recall many Bible stories that I learned during my childhood, but I haven't studied the Bible recently.
_____ I grew up in a non-Christian home. I am eager to learn all I can about the gospel.
_____ My relationship with God is personal and private. I don't discuss it with anyone.
_____ I am not convinced the Bible has the answers to my problems.
_____ I know Jesus is the Answer to every problem I have.

◆ Why Should I Follow Jesus? ◆

"What I want to know, Denny, is why would anybody want to follow Jesus?" Bruce asked straightforwardly. It was Monday after work, and Bruce and Denny had stopped by a noisy restaurant to eat dinner and watch the ball game on the restaurant's big-screen TV. The subject of religion came up during dinner. Denny was trying to explain his newfound faith to Bruce, but Bruce was belligerent.

"From what I hear you telling me, it sounds as though you are giving up quite a lot to follow this Jesus thing," Bruce said.

"It's not a Jesus thing, Bruce," Denny corrected him. It's a relationship that I have with Jesus."

"A relationship, huh? Well, you and I have a relationship, don't we? Aren't we best friends?"

"Sure, Bruce."

"But I don't ask you to stop sleeping around with women or to start going to church all the time just to be my friend. I accept you for who you are."

"Don't misunderstand, Bruce. Jesus accepts us just the way we are, too; the changes I've made have all been extremely positive. Think about it. So I don't sleep around anymore, what am I missing? AIDS? Another meaningless relationship? Hey, nice guys may sleep alone at night, but at least I can sleep now that I have a clean conscience. And

yes, I do go to church," Denny continued, "but it's not because I have to go. I want to go. I enjoy being with other Christians. And I love studying the Bible and learning more about Christ. Anything wrong with that?"

"No, no," Bruce conceded. "But like I said before, why would anyone want to follow Jesus? You talk about love, joy, peace—I have those things in my life. I have a good job, great friends, a sharp car, a few bucks in the bank, and I'm at peace with myself . . . at least I am most of the time. So why would I want to be a Christian? Tell me the truth, what's in it for me?"

◆ ◆ ◆ ◆ ◆ ◆ ◆ ◆ ◆

Be honest, now. Do you ever wonder what you are going to get out of following Jesus? You're not alone. Most of us have had similar questions at one time or another.

We know we should follow Jesus because He is the way to eternal life and He is worthy of our praise and service. Nevertheless, a nagging concern often creeps up in our minds: Am I missing out on the "good life" because I have decided to follow Jesus?

Part of the problem is that we are used to receiving immediate accolades, applause, or awards for our good deeds. If we do what is right, we expect to be rewarded.

But when it comes to following Jesus, much of our reward remains in the future. Although He fills our present lives with love, joy, peace, forgiveness, and purpose, Paul tells us what we have received in Christ now is only a down payment on all the good things He has waiting for us (Eph. 1:3–14). So don't allow yourself to get discouraged; the best is yet to come! ◆

WHAT'S IN IT FOR ME?

Do you ever wonder what you're going to get out of following Christ? Peter and the other disciples wondered. "We have left all and followed You," Peter told Jesus. "Therefore what shall we have?" (Matt. 19:27). In other words, "What's the payoff? What's in this for me?"

Paul describes some of the "payoff" for believers here in Ephesians 1:3–14. Because so much of it lies in the future, in another mode of existence, the language is strange and hard to understand. But in verse 11 he mentions an inheritance that is coming to us. What is it that we are going to receive "in Christ"?

Simply this: all that God has prepared for Christ in "the fullness of the times" is going to be ours as well (Rom. 8:15–17). This includes salvation from sin (Heb. 1:14), everlasting life (Matt. 19:29), and the kingdom of God (Matt. 25:34). In fact, we will inherit God Himself.

Is this just wishful thinking? No, God is already giving us glimpses of that inconceivable future. The Holy Spirit lives inside us as a guarantee of things to come (v. 14). He "seals" us, assuring that we remain in God's family and do not lose our inheritance. And while we move toward that day, He works within our lives to make us like Christ.

Ephesians 1:3–14

³Blessed *be* the God and Father of our Lord Jesus Christ, who has blessed us with every spiritual blessing in the heavenly *places* in Christ, ⁴just as He chose us in Him before the foundation of the world, that we should be holy and without blame before Him in love, ⁵having predestined us to adoption as sons by Jesus Christ to Himself, according to the good pleasure of His will, ⁶to the praise of the glory of His grace, by which He made us accepted in the Beloved.

⁷In Him we have redemption through His blood, the forgiveness of sins, according to the riches of His grace ⁸which He made to abound toward us in all wisdom and prudence, ⁹having made known to us the mystery of His will, according to His good pleasure which He purposed in Himself, ¹⁰that in the dispensation of the fullness of the times He might gather together in one all things in Christ, both which are in heaven and which are on earth—in Him. ¹¹In Him also we have obtained an inheritance, being predestined according to the purpose of Him who works all things according to the counsel of His will, ¹²that we who first trusted in Christ should be to the praise of His glory.

¹³In Him you also *trusted,* after you heard the word of truth, the gospel of your salvation; in whom also, having believed, you were sealed with the Holy Spirit of promise, ¹⁴who is the guarantee of our inheritance until the redemption of the purchased possession, to the praise of His glory.

1. Many people keep their "radios" tuned in to the ever-popular station WIII-FM (What Is In It For Me?). Just for fun, list the top three song titles you might hear on WIII-FM.

_____

_____

_____

2. How does the fact that God "chose us in Him" even before He created the world (Eph. 1:4) make you feel?

_____

_____

_____

3. What gifts are now yours because of the blood of Jesus Christ (1:7)?

_____

_____

_____

——◆ Do You Really Know Him? ◆——

Most of Cathy's friends were aware of her tendency to exaggerate, so they weren't surprised when she returned from her trip to Nashville claiming to have gotten to know a famous country crooner.

"Really, you guys," Cathy gushed, "Billy is so-o-oo nice! He's even sweeter in person than he is in concert or during television interviews."

Cathy's coworkers remained unconvinced, so the chagrined fan promised to produce proof of her friendship with the superstar. The next day Cathy brought an autographed eight-by-ten inch glossy photograph of the singer to work. Sure enough, it was signed, "To Cathy—Love, Billy."

"See!" Cathy said defiantly. "I told you I know him."

"Big deal!" one of her friends replied. "That picture is no proof of anything. How long did you have to stand in line to get it?"

"About forty-five minutes," Cathy admitted reluctantly.

"You don't really know him, do you, Cathy?"

"Well, I did meet him in the autograph line," Cathy protested. "And I have all of his albums and videos, and I've read every article I can get my hands on about him. And he really did ask me how I was doing, while he signed his photograph. I feel like I know him!"

"Cathy," one of her friends responded. "there's a big difference between knowing *about* someone, and really *knowing* that person."

◆ ◆ ◆ ◆ ◆ ◆ ◆ ◆ ◆

Cathy's mistake is obvious, yet many people make a similar error when it comes to knowing God. They think that because they have gone to church a few times or have read bits and pieces of the Bible, they know God. But that's not necessarily true! You can have stacks of factual information about God filed away in your mind, but not have a personal relationship with Him. When you really know someone, you know many things about that person—that person's goals, concerns, and joys. You know that person's heart.

How about you? Do you know a lot of information about God, or do you really know God? ◆

KNOWING *ABOUT* GOD IS NOT THE SAME AS *KNOWING* GOD

Many people have knowledge about religion, Christianity, and the Bible. But as the writer to the Hebrews warns, intellectual knowledge is not the same as vital faith. Knowing about God is not the same as having a personal relationship with Him.

This is clear from everyday relationships. Reading books on marriage is not the same as spending time with one's spouse. Knowing someone's phone number is a far cry from enjoying friendship with that person. Knowing who one's customers are is not the same as dealing with a specific customer.

In the same way, *knowing* God involves far more than knowing *about* Him. Information alone does not produce tangible faith. To be sure, right thinking is involved in faith, but faith is more

continued

continued

than mere knowledge. For example, the recipients of Hebrews knew quite a bit about the faith, such as the basic teachings about Christ, the need for repentance and for faith in God (Hebrews 6:1), and the meaning of baptism, ordination, the resurrection, and judgment (6:2).

Nevertheless, without the constant work of cultivation (watering, weeding, fertilizing, pruning), spiritual weeds soon sprout and in time take over, producing thorns rather than good fruit or grain (6:7–8). In that case, the crop (faith) is worthless and destined for burning. To avoid that outcome, diligent tending and development are required (6:11–12). Perseverance is crucial: we must never "coast" on past experience or former tidbits of knowledge.

Hebrews 6 is a stern warning and a loving appeal for renewed commitment to Christ. Are you in need of spiritual renewal? What disciplines might help you get started on making your faith vital once again? Perhaps you might:

- Establish a small group with other believers in your workplace, industry, neighborhood, or family to meet regularly for prayer and discussion on how Christ enters into everyday situations.

- Volunteer for a program to serve the needy through your church or a community service agency.

- Speak out on workplace policies, decisions, or practices that you know to be unethical or harmful to others or the environment.

- Begin a regular habit of Bible reading and study in order to apply God's Word to your life.

- Get to know people in international missions work.

- Begin patterns of prayer such as: prayer for people with whom you live and work— even those you may not like; prayers of thanksgiving for the things God has done for you and for the responsibilities He has given to you; prayers of confession and repentance for sin or areas of neglect in your life; prayers that meditate on God and His Word; prayers that express your innermost feelings and thoughts to God.

- Keep a journal of developments and changes in your life.

- Take on a task that uses ability with which God has gifted you, especially if that ability is unused or underused elsewhere in your life.

- Consider whether you have ignored, offended, or hurt someone and need to repent of your error and apologize to that person.

The point is, faith works best when it is the central unifying factor in one's life. Christ must never be just one more thing to occasionally acknowledge; rather, He must be the Lord of life and be brought into every area of life. Hebrews 6 urges us to take our faith beyond only knowing to being and doing. ◆

 Hebrews 6:1–12

¹Therefore, leaving the discussion of the elementary *principles* of Christ, let us go on to perfection, not laying again the foundation of repentance from dead works and of faith toward God, ²of the doctrine of baptisms, of laying on of hands, of resurrection of the dead, and of eternal judgment. ³And this we will do if God permits.

⁴For *it is* impossible for those who were once enlightened, and have tasted the heavenly gift, and have become partakers of the Holy Spirit, ⁵and have tasted the good word of God and the powers of the age to come, ⁶if they fall away, to renew them again to repentance, since they crucify again for themselves the Son of God, and put *Him* to an open shame.

⁷For the earth which drinks in the rain that often comes upon it, and bears herbs useful for

continued

continued
those by whom it is cultivated, receives blessing from God; 8but if it bears thorns and briers, *it is* rejected and near to being cursed, whose end *is to* be burned.

9But, beloved, we are confident of better things concerning you, yes, things that accompany salvation, though we speak in this manner. 10For God *is* not unjust to forget your work and labor of love which you have shown toward His name, *in that* you have ministered to the saints, and do minister. 11And we desire that each one of you show the same diligence to the full assurance of hope until the end, 12that you do not become sluggish, but imitate those who through faith and patience inherit the promises.

1. Which statements best reflect your relationship to God?

_____ I talk to God about every decision I make.
_____ I worship God in church.
_____ I pray to God every night.
_____ Jesus is my best friend.
_____ Whenever I get sick or in a financial bind, I talk to God.

2. Think of someone about whom you had heard a lot of stories before the two of you actually met (for instance, your in-laws). What were some of your misconceptions about that person?

_____

_____

_____

3. In Hebrews 6:1–3, believers are encouraged to quit arguing over some of the "elementary principles" of their faith in Christ. List the principles that often caused discussions among the Hebrew believers.

_____

_____

_____

4. What areas of your life would you consider to be "thorns and briers" (Heb. 6:8) that need to be weeded out so the "useful herbs" (6:7) can grow?

_____

_____

_____

——◆ Worth the Wait ◆——

In the second half of chapter 6, the writer to the Hebrews encourages us to trust God and to take Him at His Word—even when we feel as though we're taking a giant leap into a bottomless pit.

Abraham is mentioned as an example of someone who trusted God completely. He believed that God would do what He said He would do. This faith is remarkable because Abraham had little evidence that God would keep His promise. But Abraham knew he could count on God.

"GOD PROMISED TO . . ."

God has no problem committing Himself to people (Heb. 6:13). He has utter confidence that He can fulfill what He has promised. But His promises usually are not carried out for us immediately. God is not a vending machine dispensing treats at the press of a button. Nor should we expect to be able to call Him up and tell Him to send us what we need by overnight express. Like Abraham, we must receive His promises in faith, with great patience (Heb. 6:12–13).

Actually, trusting in others and waiting for them to deliver is hardly foreign to us. Most of us face that every day in the workplace. We accept contracts for products and services weeks, months, or even years in advance of actual delivery.

Are you asking God to deliver on your time schedule? God wants to *grow* you rather than just *give* to you. He cultivates faith and perseverance by doing His work in our lives in His way and in His time.

 Hebrews 6:13–20

13For when God made a promise to Abraham, because He could swear by no one greater, He swore by Himself, 14saying, "Surely blessing I will bless you, and multiplying I will multiply you." 15And so, after he had patiently endured, he obtained the promise. 16For men indeed swear by the greater, and an oath for confirmation is for them an end of all dispute. 17Thus God, determining to show more abundantly to the heirs of promise the immutability of His counsel, confirmed *it* by an oath, 18that by two immutable things, in which it is impossible for God to lie, we might have strong consolation, who have fled for refuge to lay hold of the hope set before *us*.

19This *hope* we have as an anchor of the soul, both sure and steadfast, and which enters the Presence *behind* the veil, 20where the forerunner has entered for us, *even* Jesus, having become High Priest forever according to the order of Melchizedek.

1. Think about some of the special moments in your life when you had to wait for what seemed like forever before you finally received a promised item. How did you feel when you:

Received your first bicycle?

Received your driver's license?

_____

Went on your first date?

_____

2. In Hebrews 6:13–18, we are told that God's promises are confirmed contracts because of two unchangeable things. What are they?

_____

_____

_____

3. In what way is God growing faith and perseverance in you right now?

_____

_____

_____

——◆ Indecent Proposals ◆——

Curt gently placed his hand on Rhonda's hand as they talked. "Look, Rhonda," he said softly, "I'm not asking you to divorce Bob. I'm just asking you to think of yourself for once. You're always worried about doing what everyone else wants; now it's time for you to do what you want. Spend the weekend with me. Bob is away on business; he'll never find out. Besides you and I both know Bob is so obsessed with his business, he probably won't even call home. He's not concerned about meeting your needs. All he cares about is himself."

Rhonda stared at Curt's hand on her own. In her heart, she knew what Curt was suggesting was absolutely wrong. It went against everything she believed in and everything she'd been taught by her parents and at church. On the other hand, Curt was right about one thing. Bob didn't care about her. All he cared about was making more money and building a bigger name for himself. He'd never find out about Curt, and even if he did, Rhonda doubted whether Bob would care. After all, she was only human. She had needs, too, and Bob wasn't worried about meeting them. Rhonda shrugged her shoulders and reached for her purse. *Hey, I never claimed to be perfect,* she thought. ◆

NOBODY'S PERFECT

It's common today for people to excuse their faults with the attitude, "Hey, nobody's perfect!" True enough. People can only be expected to be human—and that means fallible.

Unfortunately, though, few people take that reality seriously enough. Indeed, when it comes to their standing before God, all too many take a different stance: they may not be perfect, but they're "good enough."

The question is, are they good enough for God? Romans 3 says they are not. That's what Paul means when he writes, "all are under sin" (v. 9) and then cites a number of Old Testament passages to back up his claim (vv. 10–18).

It's not that people are evil through and through, or that they never do any moral good. Quite the contrary. People are capable of impressive acts of courage, compassion, and justice. But in light of God's holy (morally perfect) character, which is the ultimate standard against which people's goodness is measured, people are indeed far from perfect. Their good behavior turns out to be the exception rather than the rule.

The good news that Paul writes about in Romans, however, is that God has reached out to humanity despite its imperfect ways. His attitude has not been one of rejection, as if to say, "They're not good enough for Me," but one of grace and compassion that says, in effect, "I will make them into good people— people as good as I AM—by means of Christ My Son."

 Romans 3:9–26

⁹What then? Are we better *than they*? Not at all. For we have previously charged both Jews and Greeks that they are all under sin.

10 As it is written:
"There is none righteous, no, not one;
11 There is none who understands;
There is none who seeks after God.
12 They have all turned aside;
They have together become unprofitable;
There is none who does good, no, not one."
13 "Their throat *is* an open tomb;
With their tongues they have practiced deceit";
"The poison of asps *is* under their lips";
14 "Whose mouth *is* full of cursing and bitterness."
15 "Their feet *are* swift to shed blood;
16 Destruction and misery *are* in their ways;
17 And the way of peace they have not known."
18 "There is no fear of God before their eyes."

¹⁹Now we know that whatever the law says, it says to those who are under the law, that every mouth may be stopped, and all the world may become guilty before God. ²⁰Therefore by the deeds of the law no flesh will be justified in His sight, for by the law *is* the knowledge of sin.

²¹But now the righteousness of God apart from the law is revealed, being witnessed by the Law and the Prophets, ²²even the righteousness of God, through faith in Jesus Christ, to all and on all who believe. For there is no difference; ²³for all have sinned and fall short of the glory of God, ²⁴being justified freely by His grace through the redemption that is in Christ Jesus, ²⁵whom God set forth *as* a propitiation by His blood, through faith, to demonstrate His righteousness, because in His forbearance God had passed over the sins that were previously committed, ²⁶to demonstrate at the present time His righteousness, that He might be just and the justifier of the one who has faith in Jesus.

While some people feel frustrated that they can never quite measure up to God's stan-dards, many others test His good will by sinning deliberately and assuming that God will forgive them, no matter what. Their logic is, Well, I know I'm not perfect, but at least I'm not a bad as some other people I know!

The truth is, God does not have a rating system for sin. The Bible says we have all sinned and we all "fall short of the glory of God" (Rom. 3:23); the degree of sin is not the issue. In God's eyes, sin is sin and all sin is equally repulsive to Him. Every sin carries with it the poten-tial to ruin your life and to destroy your relationship with God, unless you repent of that sin and seek God's forgiveness.

◆ ◆ ◆ ◆ ◆ ◆ ◆ ◆ ◆ ◆

1. In Romans 3:9–18, Paul presents the hopelessness of our own efforts as a means of achiev-ing righteousness before God. How does this picture fit with the fact that everyone is made in the image of God and is valuable to Him?

_____

_____

2. How do you usually respond when someone correctly accuses you of wrongdoing? Check all that apply.

_____ I make excuses for my conduct or attitudes.
_____ I confess my faults and ask forgiveness.
_____ I say, "Everyone else is doing it!"
_____ I deny it.

3. How can you be "justified" (Rom. 3:23–24), as if you had never sinned?

_____

_____

_____

4. What steps can you take to decrease sin's effect in your life?

_____

_____

_____

◆ ◆ ◆ ◆ ◆ ◆ ◆ ◆ ◆

We live in a hustle-bustle world where most people want all they can get, and they want it now. But the Christian life doesn't work that way. Jesus is not calling you merely to have a fresh revelation of God. No, Jesus is calling you to follow Him, to commit yourself to Him for the long haul, and to put His principles to work in your life on a daily basis. He is interested in your spiritual growth and your development of character, not your accumulation of material possessions.

People often wonder why we must make changes in our character to follow Jesus. After all, aren't people "basically good"? It is a common belief that the moral problems of today are society's fault, not the individual's.

The Bible, however, offers a different view. While humans are inherently valuable, each of us is born "in sin." We have a natural tendency to do the wrong things.

It is for this reason that we need to change our character. The first step in making this change is admitting our sins and trusting God completely to forgive us.

Nobody is "good enough" to get into the kingdom of God on individual merit. When you have faith and trust in Christ, amazing things will begin to happen in your life. You will experience a peace in your heart and mind that the world can never provide. You can lay your head down on your pillow at night and know that you are forgiven.

Sleep well tonight. Tomorrow God will call you to take your faith into one of the most difficult mission fields in the world—your workplace.

FAITH AT WORK

The rain streamed down on a gloomy Monday morning as Tom weaved through the relentless stop-and-go traffic. *I should have called in sick, he thought.* But the pile of work on his office desk loomed larger than life in his mind. Besides, he was up for evaluation and his performance today might make or break his chances for a raise. Inclement weather or not, Tom had no choice.

Still, he wondered if it were really worth it. The stress of his job was getting to him; more and more Tom found himself looking out the window, mulling over why he ever chose this career in the first place. *What's the point? I'm not making any difference in the world.*

As Tom pulled into the office parking lot, he braced himself for another mayhem-filled Monday morning, and prayed, "God, please let Friday get here quickly this week."

◆ ◆ ◆ ◆ ◆ ◆ ◆ ◆ ◆

Have you ever felt like Tom? Unfortunately, many Christians share his perspective. We wonder why we slave away at a job that contributes little to the present world, and has even less eternal significance. Why bother? we wonder. We want our lives to count for Christ, but so much of what we spend our time, energy, and effort doing

in the workplace seems spiritually unfruitful and pointless. After all, how much eternal significance is there to working on an assembly line, or pushing a pencil, or helping a couple decide what sort of sofa they want to buy?

Many Christians feel that the only time their work matters to God and has true meaning is when they are doing "church work" or serving some charitable cause. Some believers have even gone so far as to change vocations, thinking that they could serve God better as a pastor or a missionary than they could at their present "secular" jobs.

While God calls some of us to serve as pastors, evangelists, teachers, and missionaries, He calls many more of us to be doctors, factory workers, politicians, building contractors, secretaries, dentists, authors, sales clerks, teachers, and so on.

Confusion about the spiritual value of our occupations,

along with many other myths concerning the nature and value of work in our society, tend to foster bad attitudes among believers in the workplace. Other believers mistakenly believe that work is a curse, resulting from God's judgment of Adam and Eve.

Still others err in another direction. They see work as the ultimate means to personal satisfaction. They receive their sense of purpose and value as a person from what they do rather than who they are. As such, they chase after financial success or prestige in the workplace as if their work were all that mattered in life.

Where is the balance? What is a proper attitude toward the workplace? Why does God care about your work? Before we look more carefully at these issues, let's see if we can unmask some of the more common workplace myths.

WORKPLACE MYTHS

Paul called himself one of God's "fellow workers" (1 Cor. 3:9). In a similar way, every one of us is a coworker with God. Yet certain distorted views of work have taken on mythical proportions in Western culture. They've had devastating effects on both the people and the message of Christ. Here's a sampling of these pernicious myths, along with a few points of rebuttal:

Myth: Church work is the only work that has any real spiritual value.

In other words, everyday work in the "secular" world counts for nothing of lasting value. Only "sacred" work matters to God.

Fact: Christianity makes no distinction between the "sacred" and the "secular."

All of life is to be lived under Christ's lordship. So when it comes to work, all work has essential value to God, and workers will answer to Him for how they have carried out the work He has given to them (1 Cor. 3:13).

Myth: The heroes of the faith are ministers and missionaries. "Lay" workers remain second-class.

This follows from the previous idea. If "sacred" work is the only work with eternal value, then "sacred workers" (clergy) are the most valuable workers. The best that "laypeople" can do is to support the clergy and engage in "ministry" during their spare hours.

Fact: God has delegated His work to everybody, not just clergy.

Among the main characters of Scripture are ranchers, farmers, fishermen, vintners, ironworkers, carpenters, tentmakers, textile manufacturers, public officials, construction supervisors and workers, military personnel, financiers, physicians, judges, tax collectors, musicians, sculptors, dancers, poets, and writers, among others. Nowhere does God view these people or their work as "second class" or "secular." Rather, their work accomplishes God's

continued

continued

work in the world. As we do our work each day, we reflect the very image of God, who is a working God. He spent six days working on the creation (Gen. 1:31—2:3), so we merely follow God's example when we work five or six days out of the week.

Myth: Work is a part of the curse.

According to this belief, God punished Adam and Eve for their sin by laying the burden of work on them: "In the sweat of your face you shall eat bread till you return to the ground" (Gen. 3:19). That's why work is so often drudgery, and why the workplace is driven by greed and selfishness.

Fact: Work is a gift from God.

The Bible never calls work a curse, but rather a gift from God (Eccl. 3:13; 5:18–19). God gave Adam and Eve work to do long before they ever sinned (Gen. 2:15), and He commends and commands work long after the fall (Gen. 9:1–7; Col. 3:23; 1 Thess. 4:1).

Myth: God is no longer involved in His creation.

For many, if not most, modern-day workers, God is irrelevant in the workplace. He may exist, but He has little to do with everyday matters of the work world. These people don't care much about what God does, and they assume He doesn't care much about what they do, either.

Fact: God remains intimately connected with both His world and its workers.

Scripture knows nothing of a detached Creator. He actively holds the creation together (Col. 1:16–17) and works toward its ultimate restoration from sin (John 5:17; Rom. 8:18–25). He uses the work of people to accomplish many of His purposes. Indeed, believers ultimately work for Christ as their Boss. He takes an active interest in how they do their work (Titus 2:9–10).

Myth: You only go around once in life—so you better make the most of it!

This is the "heaven can wait" perspective. Here-and-now is what matters; it's where the excitement is. Heaven is just a make-believe world of gold-paved streets and never-ending choirs. Boring! Why not enjoy your reward right now? Go for it!

Fact: God is saving the greatest rewards for eternity—and work will be among them.

Scripture doesn't offer much detail about life after death, but it does promise a future society remade by God where work goes on—without the sweat, toil, pain, or futility of the curse (Is. 65:17–25; Rev. 22:2–5). And as for the question of rewards, God plans to hand out rewards for how believers have spent their lives—including their work (1 Cor. 3:9–15).

Myth: The most important day of the week is Friday.

"Thank God it's Friday!" the secular work ethic cries. Because work is drudgery, weekends are for escaping—and catching up. There's no idea of a Sabbath, just a couple of days of respite from the grinding routine.

Fact: God wants us to pursue cycles of meaningful work and restorative rest.

A biblical view of work places a high value on rest. God never intended us to work seven days a week. He still invites us to join Him in a day of rest, renewal, and celebration. That restores us to go back to our work with a sense of purpose and mission. "Thank God it's Monday!" we can begin to say. ◆

1 Corinthians 3:9–11

⁹For we are God's fellow workers; you are God's field, *you are* God's building. ¹⁰According to the grace of God which was given to me, as a wise master builder I have laid the foundation, and an-other builds on it. But let each one take heed how he builds on it. ¹¹For no other foundation can anyone lay than that which is laid, which is Jesus Christ.

Where Is My Workplace?

Obviously, your job—the place where you earn your income—is your workplace. For millions of mothers and homemakers who do not receive financial remuneration for their long hours of work, the workplace may be their home, the local Parent-Teacher Organization, the Post Office, the Little League field, ballet or music lessons, the grocery store, or an endless variety of other locations in which they regularly interact with the world.

Many retired persons, volunteer workers, and civic-minded individuals may not make money at their workplace, but they put in as much time, energy, and heartfelt effort as if they were the highest-paid employees in a company.

Your workplace is wherever you spend the majority of your time interacting with society. And, it is into the workplace that our heavenly Father invites us to re-present Jesus, showing the world who Jesus is and what a difference He can make in someone's life.

◆ ◆ ◆ ◆ ◆ ◆ ◆ ◆ ◆

1. What is your attitude toward the time you spend in your workplace? Check all that apply.

_____ It's a living.

_____ I punch in; I punch out. Everything in between is irrelevant.

_____ My work is my life; without it, I'd feel empty and meaningless.

_____ I see my workplace as a mission field. God has put me there to tell other people about Jesus.

_____ I take pride in my work. It is an extension of who I am.

_____ I want my attitudes, actions, and workmanship to glorify God.

2. In 1 Corinthians 3:9, Paul refers to us as "God's fellow workers." What do you suppose Paul means by that?

_____

_____

_____

_____

3. Paul compares God's work in and through your life to a "field" and a "building." What do these two illustrations hint at in regard to the process involved in your spiritual life and your effectiveness as God's witness?

_____

_____

_____

_____

4. How would you describe your "field"?

_____ Productive
_____ Full of weeds and stones
_____ In need of nurturing
_____ Extremely fruitful

5. How would you describe your "building"?

_____ Under construction
_____ A firm foundation and a solid construction
_____ Bulging at the sides
_____ In need of renovation

◆ Work: It's What You Make It ◆

There once was a man who worked as a janitor for a large church. Every week, the man made his rounds, working nonstop to ensure that every inch of the church was spotless. He swept and polished floors, emptied all the trash, cleaned the windows, and put chairs and other items back in their proper places.

On Fridays, the janitor devoted all his time to making the sanctuary shine. He straightened the Bibles and hymnals in every pew. He swept and polished the floors. He cleaned every inch of the stained glass until the sunlight gleamed through them.

When there was a special event during the week or on a Saturday, the janitor was always there to clean up once everyone had left. He never complained about the extra work.

One day, a member of the church noticed the janitor's devotion to his work and asked him, "Don't you get tired of always being here to clean up after everyone else?"

The peaceful man looked at her with smiling eyes and said, "How could I possibly get tired of taking care of God's house?"

◆ ◆ ◆ ◆ ◆ ◆ ◆ ◆ ◆

What a difference an attitude makes! One person looks at work as mundane, grueling toil; another person is doing something great for God. How about you? What is your attitude toward your work? Is your work a curse or a blessing? ◆

Is Work a Curse?

What was the curse that God put on creation (Rom. 8:20)? One of the most stubborn myths in Western culture is that God imposed work as a curse to punish Adam and Eve's sin (Gen. 3:1–19). As a result, some people view work as something evil. Scripture does not support that idea:

God Himself is a worker. The fact that God works shows that work is not evil, since by definition God cannot do evil. On the contrary, work is an activity that God carries out.

God created people in His image to be His coworkers. He gives us ability and authority to manage His creation.

God established work before the fall. Genesis 1–2 record how God created the world. The account tells how He placed the first humans in a garden "to tend and keep it" (2:15). This work assignment was given before sin entered the world and God pronounced the curse (Gen. 3). Obviously, then, work cannot be a result of the fall since people were working before the fall.

God commends work even after the fall. If work were evil in and of itself, God would never encourage people to engage in it.

But He does. For example, He told Noah and his family the same thing He told Adam and Eve—to have dominion over the earth (Gen. 9:1–7). In the New Testament, Christians are commanded to work (Col. 3:23; 1 Thess. 4:11).

Work itself was not cursed in the fall. A careful reading of Genesis 3:17–19 shows that God cursed the *ground* as a result of Adam's sin—but not work:

"Cursed is the ground for
   your sake;
In toil you shall eat of it
All the days of your life.
Both thorns and thistles it
   shall bring forth for you,
And you shall eat the herb of
   the field.
In the sweat of your face you
   shall eat bread
Till you return to the ground,
For out of it you were taken;
For dust you are,
And to dust you shall return."

Notice three ways that this curse affected work: (1) Work had been a joy, but now it would be "toil." People would feel burdened down by it, and even come to hate it. (2) "Thorns and thistles" would hamper people's efforts to exercise dominion. In other words, the earth would not be as cooperative as it had been. (3) People would have to "sweat" to accomplish their tasks. Work would require enormous effort and energy.

Most of us know all too well how burdensome work can be. Workplace stresses and pressures, occupational hazards, the daily grind, office politics, crushing boredom, endless routine, disappointments, setbacks, catastrophes, frustration, cutthroat competition, fraud, deception, injustice—there is no end of evils connected with work. But work itself is not evil. Far from naming it a curse, the Bible calls work and its fruit a gift from God (Eccl. 3:13; 5:18–19). ◆

Romans 8:19–21

[19]For the earnest expectation of the creation eagerly waits for the revealing of the sons of God. [20]For the creation was subjected to futility, not willingly, but because of Him who subjected *it* in hope; [21]because the creation itself also will be delivered from the bondage of corruption into the glorious liberty of the children of God.

1. An architect may design churches, as well as prisons or banks. A free-lance writer may write travel stories for a secular journal in addition to writing articles for Christian magazines. Is one aspect of their work more "spiritual" than another? Explain.

_____

_____

_____

_____

2. Adam and Eve's sin and God's subsequent curse of the ground affected work in at least three ways. How do these three conditions still exist in your workplace?

_____

_____

_____

3. If your work is a gift from God, what are some ways you can express your thanks to Him?

_____

_____

_____

◆ Dedication to the Job ◆

Fred received an award from his company for twenty years of perfect attendance at work. To Fred, perfect attendance not only meant never being absent from work, but also never even being late for work! Fred achieved his twenty-year record by battling imposing weather, troublesome cars, and occasional illnesses to make his daily twenty-mile commute from home to work.

The award for this outstanding record inspired Fred. He thought, *If I can make twenty years, why not twenty-one?* He continued to extend his perfect attendance record, day after day, year after year. The biggest threat to his record came when a blizzard dumped fourteen inches of snow on his street. Fred recalls, "I got up at 3:30 that morning and shov-

eled two tracks for the car. I was supposed to start work at 8:00, but I was there at 6:30."

✦ ✦ ✦ ✦ ✦ ✦ ✦ ✦

By the time Fred finally retired, he had established a perfect attendance record of thirty successive years. Now that's dedication to the job!

But, believe it or not, another worker has a record that even surpasses that of Fred's. This worker puts in long hours

every day. In fact, He works around-the-clock. He never takes a day off because of illness, nor does He take a vacation. He doesn't ask His workers to do anything He wouldn't do, and He has a reputation for being a gracious employer and coworker. This hard worker is busy among us, right here and right now. We know this worker—He is God. ◆

GOD—THE ORIGINAL WORKER

God is a worker! Perhaps you've never thought of Him that way. But that's how He first appears in Scripture. In the creation account (Gen. 1–2) He wears no end of occupational hats: strategic planner, designer, civil engineer, real estate developer, project manager, artist, and many more. Using these skills, He created something that was "very good" (1:31). How good? As good as God! No wonder the creation is said to "glorify," or praise God. His work is worth honoring, and it honors Him.

Furthermore, God continues to work (John 5:17), maintaining the creation and providing for His creatures. He also carries out the work of salvation. And He uses people to help Him accomplish these tasks. Think what that means:

(1) *Work itself is inherently good.* God didn't mind "getting

His hands dirty," so to speak, in creating the universe. Genesis says He "worked" to bring it into existence (2:2). But that means work must be good in and of itself, since by definition, God can only do what is good. It also means work reflects the activity of God. The engineer who designs a bridge, the zoologist who

studies animals, and the farmer who raises crops all carry out jobs that God did at the beginning of the world.

(2) *Your work is important; it matters.* The work that God gives you has dignity to it. In fact, God created you "in His image" (Gen. 1:26–27). Just as He works, so He has created you to work. Genesis even says that God has placed human beings in authority over the creation as His managers. As you use the abilities He's given you, you can be a partner, a coworker with Him to carry out His work.

For example, God can use: the nurse to meet the health needs of patients; the grocer to distribute food to customers; the researcher to provide accurate

continued

continued
information; the lawyer to promote justice for clients; the career homemaker to nurture growing children. God values these kinds of jobs because they help to carry out His purposes in the world. These things matter to Him.

(3) *There's no such thing as "secular" or "sacred" work.* God certainly uses ministers and missionaries to meet spiritual and personal needs around the world. But they are not the only people doing "God's work." God is just as interested in the physical, emotional, intellectual, and other needs that people have. He also cares about the management of the earth itself. It takes all kinds of skills, and all kinds of people, to do what God wants done in the world.

(4) *You should do your work in a way that honors God.* Your work has dignity; you're created in God's image as a worker; you're a coworker with God; you have God-given abilities to carry out important tasks that He wants done. All of this says that what you do for work and how you do it should bring glory to God. He should be pleased with it—and with you as you do it. ◆

 John 5:17

[17]But Jesus answered them, "My Father has been working until now, and I have been working."

1. Imagine that you and Jesus are working together on the same project. How would His presence influence your actions and attitudes in your workplace? Check all that apply.

_____ I'd be more conscientious about the quality of my work.
_____ I'd have to wash out my mouth with soap.
_____ I'd be on time for work.
_____ I wouldn't be making or receiving personal phone calls on company time.
_____ I wouldn't be using the company car for my personal travel.
_____ I'd do my job to the best of my ability.

2. The Bible says you are made in the image of God (Gen. 1:27). Scripture also says that you are God's workmanship (Eph. 2:10). As such, what are some ways your work can reflect God's image?

_____

_____

_____

3. How does your work impact your sense of dignity?

_____

_____

_____

4. From a biblical perspective, why is it "abnormal" for people not to be working at something, regardless of whether or not they are being financially compensated?

_____

_____

_____

——◆ Another One of Those Days! ◆——

Have you ever had "one of those days," where from the time you woke up, you just knew that it was going to be a bad day?
- *You know it's going to be a bad day when you wake up to discover that your waterbed broke. Then you remember that you don't have a waterbed!*
- *You know it's going to be a bad day when you put your blue jeans on backwards . . . and they fit better!*
- *You know it's going to be a bad day when your four-year-old tells you that it is almost impossible to flush a grapefruit down the toilet!*

We've all had one of those days. You go to work, seeing nothing but the negative side of everything and everybody in your workplace. Your work is mundane and lacks real meaning; the report you need to do for your supervisor is irrelevant; nobody seems to appreciate your contribution to the team effort; the people with whom you work are rude. I'd have been better off just pulling the covers up and staying in bed today, you pout.

But, wait! Do you want to change that bad attitude and negative thinking? You can. Just stop for a moment and ask yourself, "Who am I really working for, anyhow? The boss? The company? The country? The good of mankind?" No, the Bible says that ultimately you are working for Jesus. He is the One whom you should seek to please. He is the reason you got out of bed today, and it is to Christ that you will eventually give an account for how well you performed your duties in the workplace.

You can honor God through your conscientious work, your commitment to excellence, and your willingness to contribute to the overall effort of your employer and your fellow employees. God is the One who gave you the ability to work in the first place. Whatever you do, don't just work for the pay or the approval of your peers or your employer; do your work to please God.

 Colossians 3:22–24

[22]Bondservants, obey in all things your masters according to the flesh, not with eyeservice, as men-pleasers, but in sincerity of heart, fearing God. [23]And whatever you do, do it heartily, as to the Lord and not to men, [24]knowing that from the Lord you will receive the reward of the inheritance; for you serve the Lord Christ.

WHO'S THE BOSS?

He had a menial, dead-end job. They assigned him tasks that no one else wanted—the "dumb-work," the dirty work, the dangerous work. They called him out at all hours of the day and night to satisfy the whims of his supervisors. He had little hope for advancement. In fact, he'd be lucky just to keep his job; plenty of others stood in line, ready to replace him. Whether he even lived or died mattered little. He was a first-century Roman slave.

Yet he mattered to God, and his work mattered, too. In writing to this lowly worker (Col. 3:22–24), Paul redefined his occupational status: he was not just a Roman slave, he was an employee of Christ the Lord! That makes all the difference.

So it is for any Christian in the workplace. You may work for a giant multinational corporation or a mom-'n-pop pizza parlor. You may have 15 levels of bureaucracy over you, or be self-employed. It doesn't matter. Ultimately, Christ is your Boss. Consider what that means:

Christ gives you work to do. *Work is a gift from God. He has created you in His image to be a worker, giving you skills and abilities to accomplish His purposes. He has also sovereignly placed you in your occupation to do His work there. Even if your job is as lowly as a Roman slave's, it still has value and dignity to Christ.*

Christ is your Boss, but He uses human supervisors. *According to Colossians 3, people in authority over you are actually human representatives of Christ. They may not act*

continued

continued
very Christlike. But in working for them, you are ultimately working for Christ. Do you follow their instructions? Do you shirk your job when they're not around? Are you more interested in impressing them to gain approval and advancement than in getting the job done? How would your work ethic change if you saw Christ as your supervisor?

Christ asks you to put your heart into your work. If you serve Christ in your job, you have more rea-son than anyone else to work with integrity and enthusiasm. The job itself may be unchallenging or unpleasant. But Christ asks you to do it with dignity, to the best of your ability, as though working for Christ Himself.

Christ will reward you for good, faithful work. This passage says that Christ will review your work someday. You can expect praise and reward for working in a Christlike manner. ◆

1. In Colossians 3:22 Paul instructs believers to obey their masters. How does this principle apply to your relationship with your boss?

_____

_____

_____

_____

2. List some ways you think your attitudes and actions in your workplace will change now that you are more aware you are working for Christ.

_____

_____

_____

_____

3. In Colossians 3:24, Paul says you will receive "the reward of the inheritance" for doing your work as unto the Lord. To what reward is he referring?

_____

_____

_____

_____

◆ Worshipers at Work ◆

A young couple pulled their car into a church parking lot on Saturday morning, just as the groundskeeper was changing the information on the church's outdoor bulletin board. "Excuse me, Sir," the young man called, as he leaned his head out the car window.

The groundskeeper turned and smiled when he saw the couple. "Yes? Can I help you?"

"We were wondering," said the young man, "if you could please tell us what time tomorrow's worship service begins?"

The groundskeeper answered with a twinkle in his eye, "Well, the worship begins at 10:00, but the service begins somewhere around 12:15."

◆ ◆ ◆ ◆ ◆ ◆ ◆ ◆ ◆

The groundskeeper's point was that the congregation gathered in the church building on Sunday morning from ten o'clock until around noon. But the Church—the Body of Christ—moved out of the sanctuary and into the world to serve and represent Christ every day of the week, wherever any of the believers went.

Many Christians go to church on Sunday; they sing, read the Bible, pray, and listen to a sermon. But when they leave the church parking lot, they often forget to take their faith *with them. Many believers unwittingly disconnect their relationship with God from what they call "the real world," in which they must live and work the rest of the week.*

Let's face it—on Monday morning, it's tough to maintain the spiritual momentum you felt on Sunday morning. But what is a believer to do? The members of the early church quickly discovered a workable cycle of spiritual refreshment and growth, followed by periods of wrestling with real world responsibilities. Let's take a look at how they maintained spiritual equilibrium in an unstable world—a world much like our own. ◆

RECONNECTING SUNDAY AND MONDAY

D oes the faith you celebrate on Sunday sometimes feel disconnected from the "real world" you face on Monday? The newly formed group of believers (Acts 2:46–47) closed that gap by practicing a rhythm of two kinds of experiences—gathering for growth and worship balanced by scattering into the world for work and to communicate the gospel to non-Christian friends and coworkers.

Look at the chart on the next page. Notice the rhythm of gathering for refinement and scattering for engagement as we see it progressing in Acts 4–9.

This pattern continues throughout Acts as the narrative moves back and forth between internal meetings of the church and external encounters with the surrounding culture. The account includes more than twenty refinement narratives and more than fifty engagement narratives. We clearly see a connection between the development of faith and its delivery.

continued

continued

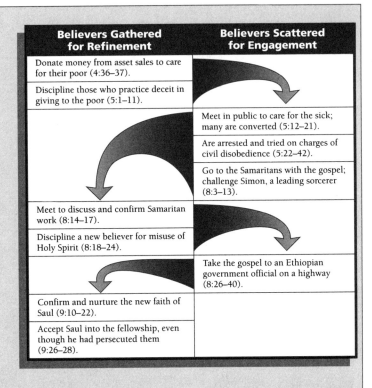

Believers Gathered for Refinement	Believers Scattered for Engagement
Donate money from asset sales to care for their poor (4:36–37).	
Discipline those who practice deceit in giving to the poor (5:1–11).	
	Meet in public to care for the sick; many are converted (5:12–21).
	Are arrested and tried on charges of civil disobedience (5:22–42).
	Go to the Samaritans with the gospel; challenge Simon, a leading sorcerer (8:3–13).
Meet to discuss and confirm Samaritan work (8:14–17).	
Discipline a new believer for misuse of Holy Spirit (8:18–24).	
	Take the gospel to an Ethiopian government official on a highway (8:26–40).
Confirm and nurture the new faith of Saul (9:10–22).	
Accept Saul into the fellowship, even though he had persecuted them (9:26–28).	

Believers today could help to reconnect Sundays and Mondays by moving through this same cycle. The gathering process might include worship services, praise gatherings, prayer meetings, fellowship over meals, and teaching for growth. Such encounters prepare us for Monday's world of work and responsibility, filled as it often is with pressures, conflicts, and opportunities to engage unbelievers as they inspect or perhaps even oppose our faith.

Rather than being disconnected, these two worlds need to be vitally connected. The refinement of our faith as we gather for growth supplies much-needed strength as we engage the world Monday through Saturday. On the other hand, the realities of life outside the fellowship can alert us to areas where we need to grow in faith.

Are you reconnecting Sunday and Monday by practicing this rhythm? Is there a link between the resources of your faith community and the demands of your world? Are there ways to improve the connections? ◆

Acts 2:42–47

⁴²And they continued steadfastly in the apostles' doctrine and fellowship, in the breaking of bread, and in prayers. ⁴³Then fear came upon every soul, and many wonders and signs were done through the apostles. ⁴⁴Now all who believed were together, and had all things in common, ⁴⁵and sold their possessions and goods, and divided them among all, as anyone had need.

⁴⁶So continuing daily with one accord in the temple, and breaking bread from house to house, they ate their food with gladness and simplicity of heart, ⁴⁷praising God and having favor with all the people. And the Lord added to the church daily those who were being saved.

1. How important is your church involvement to maintaining your relationship with God? Check one.

_____ The church is not important to me.
_____ I am my own church.
_____ Church is a little important to me, but not very.
_____ Church is extremely important to my spiritual growth.

2. Some Christians tend to minimize the need for church attendance to maintain their spiritual lives. Yet in Acts 2:42–47, the members of the early church constantly wanted to get together with each other. What are some reasons that might explain the change in the attitudes of many believers today?

_____

_____

_____

3. In Acts 2:42, Luke lists four spiritual activities in which the early believers regularly engaged. List these activities in order of importance for your life.

_____

_____

_____

4. What impact did the early church have on the "real world" around them as a result of their own constantly rejuvenated relationship with the Lord (Acts 2:47)?

_____

_____

_____

Living out your relationship with Christ in the workplace is not always as easy as it sounds. First you must learn to see work from God's perspective. He expects you to honor Him by doing excellent work and by maintaining a reputation for integrity, fairness, and honesty in all that you do. As a Christian, you should approach your work each day as though you were working for the Lord, because in reality, you are!

As you better understand how highly God values your work, you will find a sense of purpose that far surpasses the satisfaction you receive from getting a paycheck, or even the "warm fuzzies" you feel when you receive the appreciation of your superiors or the respect of your peers. Knowing that your work matters to God gives you that extra incentive to get out of bed each morning, cope with a car that won't start, fight traffic or a variety of other obstacles, and still walk into your workplace with a smile on your face.

Why? Because you know that you are not just killing time. You are not simply making a living. You are helping God meet the needs of the world. You are faithfully managing the resources and responsibilities that He has placed under your control. Service replaces selfishness as your motivation for what you do.

But God is not a slave driver. He does not want you to become a workaholic because of some misguided notion that you must "prove" yourself. God wants you to enjoy times of rest, relaxation, and spiritual refreshment.

When we examine some of the patterns in our lives, we discover that we do many things like Mom, Dad, or other family members did them. The older we get, the more we recognize the influence of our heritage and traditions on our own actions and attitudes. In the next chapter, we'll explore our roots to see how God has "planted" us in His kingdom to use the past and the present to bring forth fruit for eternity.

YOUR FAMILY ALBUM

Imagine that someone is going to make a movie about your family. Would there be any bizarre, annoying, or shady characters? For most of us, our cast would consist of a variety of characters, with some of them being like:

- Cousin Bob, who knows everything about everything.
- Aunt Matilda, who talks too much, eats too much, and wears far too much perfume.
- Cousin Billy, who, if he keeps trying, is going to make something of himself . . . someday . . . at least, everybody hopes so.
- Cousin Alice, for whom nothing is ever good enough.

- Uncle Joe, who tries to get everyone to invest in his "surefire" business deal.

The list could go on and on, but you love them just the same because they are, after all, family!

Even Jesus had some unusual characters in His family. Jesus descended from the well-established, royal line of King David, but His genealogy also included members of several other ethnic groups (Matt. 1:1–17). Furthermore, some of Jesus' relatives weren't exactly model citizens. Illicit sex, murder, lies, and political intrigue were all factors.

Jesus was never ashamed of His roots, though; nor did He ever degrade anyone else's family background. Jesus acknowledged the sinners in His lineage, and accepted the fact that God could bring about good even where evil was intended.

By His example, Jesus teaches us not only to acknowledge our roots, but also to accept other people, despite their tainted lines of descent or cultural differences. By accepting your roots, you can develop a better understanding of who you are and how God has wonderfully worked in your family to bring you to faith in Christ.

JESUS' ROOTS

Matthew opens with a family tree of Jesus' ancestors (1:1–16). Don't skip this genealogy and begin at verse 18! Matthew includes it for at least three important reasons:

(1) To show that God's Son was also a real, flesh-and-blood human. This was a crucial concept for Matthew's first-century readers.

(2) To show that Jesus was the long-awaited Messiah of Israel. Notice the prominence of David and Abraham.

(3) To show that Jesus is also the international Christ, the Savior of the whole world. His genealogy reaches beyond Jews to include several ethnic groups that populated the Middle East during Israel's Old Testament history. Jesus came to "make disciples of all the nations" (Matt. 28:19).

Matthew 1:1–17

¹The book of the genealogy of Jesus Christ, the Son of David, the Son of Abraham:

²Abraham begot Isaac, Isaac begot Jacob, and Jacob begot Judah and his brothers. ³Judah begot Perez and Zerah by Tamar, Perez begot Hezron, and Hezron begot Ram. ⁴Ram begot Amminadab, Amminadab begot Nahshon, and Nahshon begot Salmon. ⁵Salmon begot Boaz by Rahab, Boaz begot Obed by Ruth, Obed begot Jesse, ⁶and Jesse begot David the king.

David the king begot Solomon by her *who had been the wife* of Uriah. ⁷Solomon begot Rehoboam, Rehoboam begot Abijah, and Abijah begot Asa. ⁸Asa begot Jehoshaphat, Jehoshaphat begot Joram, and Joram begot Uzziah. ⁹Uzziah begot Jotham, Jotham begot Ahaz, and Ahaz begot Hezekiah. ¹⁰Hezekiah begot Manasseh, Manasseh begot Amon, and Amon begot Josiah. ¹¹Josiah begot Jeconiah and his brothers about the time they were carried away to Babylon.

¹²And after they were brought to Babylon, Jeconiah begot Shealtiel, and Shealtiel begot Zerubbabel. ¹³Zerubbabel begot Abiud, Abiud begot Eliakim, and Eliakim begot Azor. ¹⁴Azor begot Zadok, Zadok begot Achim, and Achim begot Eliud. ¹⁵Eliud begot Eleazar, Eleazar begot Matthan, and Matthan begot Jacob. ¹⁶And Jacob begot Joseph the husband of Mary, of whom was born Jesus who is called Christ.

¹⁷So all the generations from Abraham to David *are* fourteen generations, from David until the captivity in Babylon *are* fourteen generations, and from the captivity in Babylon until the Christ *are* fourteen generations.

WHAT IT MEANS TO BE LIKE JESUS

Jesus indicated that those who follow Him will become like Him (Matt. 10:25). What does it mean to **"be like Jesus"** *in today's complex world? Matthew paints eight portraits of what Christlikeness looks like, including:*

#1: To Be Like Jesus Means TO ACCEPT OUR ROOTS

Jesus' family tree hides nothing. His heritage was multiethnic and included several unat- tractive or embarrassing individuals. Indeed, the circumstances surrounding His own birth might have raised questions in the minds of some. But Jesus never denied His ancestry or allowed others to shame Him. If we want to be like Him, we need to understand and accept our roots in terms of culture, race, gender, and reputation. Moreover, like Jesus we want to avoid demeaning anyone else's heritage.

1. How far back can you trace your family tree?

_____

_____

2a. Who is your oldest living relative? How old is he or she?

_____

2b. List three ways in which you are similar to this person. (For instance: I share my grand-mother's love for gardening.)

_____

_____

_____

2c. List three ways in which you are different from your oldest living relative. (For instance: Uncle George was extremely prejudiced in his views concerning women, and I am not.)

_____

_____

_____

3. Matthew wrote primarily for a Jewish audience. Why do you think Jesus' genealogy would be of special interest to them?

_____

_____

_____

4. In Matthew 1:1–17, the author lists forty-six ancestors of Jesus. Some were heroes, others were scoundrels; many were simply ordinary people who loved God. What lessons do you think are implied in regard to God's ability to work in your family?

_____

_____

_____

◆ Remember Where You Came From! ◆

Julia flinched noticeably when her dad pulled two cigars from a mahogany box on the coffee table and gestured toward Steve, her fiance, whom she had brought home from college to meet her parents.

"Have a cigar, Stephen," Julia's dad offered kindly. "They're imported."

Steve took the cigar hesitantly. He usually didn't smoke, but he did not want to offend his future father-in-law. Julia's father did most of the talking, telling stories about his playing golf at the finest country clubs and sailing in the Mediterranean.

Julia noticed Steve's growing discomfort as her father quizzed him about his golf and sailing skills. Steve didn't play golf, and he had only been sailing once. Most of Steve's "free" time was spent working so he could afford to go to college.

"Dad, why don't you let Steve tell you about some of the work he's done for *World News*. He has written some very interesting articles," Julia suggested.

She was afraid this might happen. Julia didn't want Steve to be intimidated by her family, nor did she want her parents to make Steve feel unwelcome because he did not come from a wealthy family. Fortunately, her father took the hint and changed the conversation.

❖ ❖ ❖ ❖ ❖ ❖ ❖ ❖ ❖

God wants us to appreciate where we have come from and how He has worked in our families. When people from different backgrounds are brought together, they have a special opportunity to demonstrate God's desire for us to accept our differences and respect each other as human beings.

The apostle Paul is a prime example of someone who had a healthy perspective on both the good and the bad associated with his heritage. Paul valued his background as a gift from God. ◆

PAUL THE JEW—TEACHER OF THE GENTILES

What is your ethnic heritage? Are you proud to be who you are? Paul was. In 2 Timothy 1:3 he openly identifies with his background as a Jew, affirming his connection to the "forefathers," people of faith such as Abraham, Isaac, Jacob, Joseph, Moses, and David.

But wait! Didn't he earlier call that same background a "loss" and "rubbish" as he considered his new life in Christ (Phil. 3:4–8)? Yes, at times he was highly critical of his culture, but only to the extent that it fostered self-righteous pride, exclusive attitudes, or a belief in salvation by the Law rather than by faith in Christ. In other words, Paul had perspective on his roots. He was able to value his heritage for the good things it gave him, yet reject its negative legacies.

Perhaps that was why Paul was so effective as a "teacher of the Gentiles" (2 Tim. 1:11)—a remarkable calling, given his training as a Pharisee and strict adherence to Hebrew traditions. God not only helped him reevaluate his ethnicity but in the process transformed his attitude toward non-Jews. He became a man who knew who he was, so he was no longer threatened by people from other cultures.

Consequently, Paul had much to offer Timothy, who came from a mixed background (Acts 16:1–3). Paul also serves as a model for believers today who need perspective on their roots in an increasingly diverse culture where ethnic and racial tensions run high.

---

 2 Timothy 1:3–7

[3]I thank God, whom I serve with a pure conscience, as *my* forefathers *did*, as without ceasing I remember you in my prayers night and day, [4]greatly desiring to see you, being mindful of your tears, that I may be filled with joy, [5]when I call to remembrance the genuine faith that is in you, which dwelt first in your grandmother Lois and your mother Eunice, and I am persuaded is in you also. [6]Therefore I remind you to stir up the gift of God which is in you through the laying on of my hands. [7]For God has not given us a spirit of fear, but of power and of love and of a sound mind.

1. How have your parents' ethnic and religious backgrounds affected your attitudes and beliefs today?

_____

_____

_____

2. List some ways your heritage has influenced your lifestyle.

_____

_____

_____

3. Why did Paul view his Jewish background as "rubbish" on one hand, but a valuable gift from God on the other?

_____

_____

_____

4. Why do you think Paul felt he needed to give Timothy the reminder found in 2 Timothy 1:6–7?

_____

_____

_____

◆ Discovering Your Religious Roots ◆

Of all the books in the New Testament, Hebrews especially deals with heritage. The unknown author of this book celebrates Christ as the fulfillment of the Old Testament law and prophecy, while at the same time urging Hebrew believers to live out their newfound faith as Christians. Undoubtedly, the book was popular with first-century Jewish Christians who had questions about how their old faith fit with their new faith in Jesus.

The book encourages the Hebrews to honor and respect the good things from their Old Testament heritage because the foundation of their new faith is firmly rooted in Judaism. Nevertheless, they were not to live in the past; they were to press on and grow into mature believers.

Today, the book of Hebrews continues to encourage us to examine and accept the events that God has used to shape our lives. That does not mean that everything that happened to you or your family in the past was acceptable to God. It does mean that all of those things have contributed to molding you into the special person you are today.

RESEARCHING YOUR OWN RELIGIOUS ROOTS

The book of Hebrews shows that God uses history to bring people to Himself. In the case of the Jews, God used generations of people and centuries of political events and religious symbolism to prepare the way for Christ. If you are Jewish, you have much to celebrate as you ponder God's sovereignty and grace in using your ancestors the Hebrews to bless "all the families of the earth" (Gen. 12:3; 22:18; Acts 3:25–26; Gal. 3:8).

However, God's participation in history extends far beyond the Jews. In fact, every believer is indebted to God's grace for superintending the circumstances that brought the gospel to him or her.

Have you ever traced the path between Jesus' proclamation of the gospel in the first century and your reception of it today? Do you know the religious roots of your own family and ancestors? Why not examine that heritage, either on your own or with a small group of believers? Doing so will help to personalize the gospel to your own life and experience. Here are some suggestions for getting started:

Gathering the Data

Begin by collecting as much information as you can about your genealogy. Widespread interest in genealogical studies in recent years has made this process easier. Many books, articles, libraries, data bases, organizations, seminars, and other resources exist to help you. In addition, you'll want to talk with your parents, grandparents, or other relatives who might have information about your family and its heritage. As you carry out your search, consider such questions as:

- When and where did your ancestors live?

- What was their culture like?
- What historical or political events or technological developments occurred during their times? How might those have affected people?
- What was the religious climate in which your ancestors lived? For example, what was the view of God, the nature of evil, the origins of the world, and the afterlife? Was one religion dominant, or were there many alternatives? How did religion affect people's day-to-day lives?
- When was the gospel first introduced to the society in which your ancestors lived? What was the reception? What has been the legacy since?
- Are there any notable religious figures in your ancestry or connected with people in your history?
- Overall, what has been your family's posture toward the message of Christ?
- What has been the role of religion in your family of origin?

continued

continued

Where did its religious sentiments come from? Are there any surviving symbols of religion that might hold clues for investigation (family Bibles or other books, letters, documents, pictures, clothing, etc.)?

• When did you personally first hear the gospel?

Evaluating Your Religious Roots

As your knowledge about your ancestry grows, you can begin to piece together some idea of your religious heritage. Be careful not to jump to conclusions or make too much of sketchy details. You probably won't be able to come up with any definitive answers, but you can at least gain an appreciation for how God has worked in your past and what it took for Him to bring you to faith.

Of course, you may discover elements of your family's religious history that run counter to the gospel. But that, too, is important to know. You need not agree with what others believed or did in the past, but it's worth understanding the bolt of cloth from which you've been cut.

As you evaluate your data, consider such questions as:

• Is the gospel recent in your family's history, or has there been a long legacy of participation in the faith?
• If Christianity has been a part of your cultural or religious roots, what distinguishes your family's expression of Christianity from other traditions within the faith? Why? Where did that tradition come from and how and why did your family identify with it?
• What beliefs and practices among your religious roots would you disagree with or even denounce? Why?
• What has been the reception of your family to your personal faith in Christ? Why? How might the past contribute to their response?
• How might your understanding of the past affect the way in which you present the gospel to any unbelievers among your relatives?
• What is the story of how the gospel traveled from the apostles in the first century to your life today? What response can you make to God for superintending this process? ◆

 Hebrews 11:1—12:2

¹Now faith is the substance of things hoped for, the evidence of things not seen. ²For by it the elders obtained a *good* testimony.

³By faith we understand that the worlds were framed by the word of God, so that the things which are seen were not made of things which are visible.

⁴By faith Abel offered to God a more excellent sacrifice than Cain, through which he obtained witness that he was righteous, God testifying of his gifts; and through it he being dead still speaks.

⁵By faith Enoch was taken away so that he did not see death, "and was not found, because God had taken him"; for before he was taken he had this testimony, that he pleased God. ⁶But without faith *it is* impossible to please *Him,* for he who comes to God must believe that He is, and *that* He is a rewarder of those who diligently seek Him.

⁷By faith Noah, being divinely warned of things not yet seen, moved with godly fear, prepared an ark for the saving of his household, by which he condemned the world and became heir of the righteousness which is according to faith.

⁸By faith Abraham obeyed when he was called to go out to the place which he would receive as an inheritance. And he went out, not knowing where he was going. ⁹By faith he dwelt in the land of promise as *in* a foreign country, dwelling in tents with Isaac and Jacob, the heirs with him of the same promise; ¹⁰for he waited for the city which has foundations, whose builder and maker *is* God.

¹¹By faith Sarah herself also received strength to conceive seed, and she bore a child when she was past the age, because she judged Him faithful
continued

continued

who had promised. [12]Therefore from one man, and him as good as dead, were born *as many as* the stars of the sky in multitude—innumerable as the sand which is by the seashore.

[13]These all died in faith, not having received the promises, but having seen them afar off were assured of them, embraced *them* and confessed that they were strangers and pilgrims on the earth. [14]For those who say such things declare plainly that they seek a homeland. [15]And truly if they had called to mind that *country* from which they had come out, they would have had opportunity to return. [16]But now they desire a better, that is, a heavenly *country*. Therefore God is not ashamed to be called their God, for He has prepared a city for them.

[17]By faith Abraham, when he was tested, offered up Isaac, and he who had received the promises offered up his only begotten *son,* [18]of whom it was said, "In Isaac your seed shall be called," [19]concluding that God *was* able to raise *him* up, even from the dead, from which he also received him in a figurative sense.

[20]By faith Isaac blessed Jacob and Esau concerning things to come.

[21]By faith Jacob, when he was dying, blessed each of the sons of Joseph, and worshiped, *leaning* on the top of his staff.

[22]By faith Joseph, when he was dying, made mention of the departure of the children of Israel, and gave instructions concerning his bones.

[23]By faith Moses, when he was born, was hidden three months by his parents, because they saw *he was* a beautiful child; and they were not afraid of the king's command.

[24]By faith Moses, when he became of age, refused to be called the son of Pharaoh's daughter, [25]choosing rather to suffer affliction with the people of God than to enjoy the passing pleasures of sin, [26]esteeming the reproach of Christ greater riches than the treasures in Egypt; for he looked to the reward.

[27]By faith he forsook Egypt, not fearing the wrath of the king; for he endured as seeing Him who is invisible. [28]By faith he kept the Passover and the sprinkling of blood, lest he who destroyed the firstborn should touch them.

[29]By faith they passed through the Red Sea as by dry *land, whereas* the Egyptians, attempting *to do* so, were drowned.

[30]By faith the walls of Jericho fell down after they were encircled for seven days. [31]By faith the harlot Rahab did not perish with those who did not believe, when she had received the spies with peace.

[32]And what more shall I say? For the time would fail me to tell of Gideon and Barak and Samson and Jephthah, also *of* David and Samuel and the prophets: [33]who through faith subdued kingdoms, worked righteousness, obtained promises, stopped the mouths of lions, [34]quenched the violence of fire, escaped the edge of the sword, out of weakness were made strong, became valiant in battle, turned to flight the armies of the aliens. [35]Women received their dead raised to life again.

Others were tortured, not accepting deliverance, that they might obtain a better resurrection. [36]Still others had trial of mockings and scourgings, yes, and of chains and imprisonment. [37]They were stoned, they were sawn in two, were tempted, were slain with the sword. They wandered about in sheepskins and goatskins, being destitute, afflicted, tormented— [38]of whom the world was not worthy. They wandered in deserts and mountains, *in* dens and caves of the earth.

[39]And all these, having obtained a good testimony through faith, did not receive the promise, [40]God having provided something better for us, that they should not be made perfect apart from us.

CHAPTER 12

[1]Therefore we also, since we are surrounded by so great a cloud of witnesses, let us lay aside every weight, and the sin which so easily ensnares *us,* and let us run with endurance the race that is set before us, [2]looking unto Jesus, the author and finisher of *our* faith, who for the joy that was set before Him endured the cross, despising the shame, and has sat down at the right hand of the throne of God.

1. Hebrews 11 reviews many Old Testament believers who trusted God. In the first thirty-four verses, the writer records tremendous episodes of great faith linked with wonderful and often miraculous results. Then, suddenly, in verse 35 the writer shifts gears and says, "Others were tortured . . ." The account then records another group of saints who also had great faith—perhaps as much or more than the first group—but they paid horrible prices for their unwavering commitment. Why do you think the author included both groups of heroes?

_____

_____

_____

2. Why would the author's conclusion (Heb. 11:39–40) have surprised his Jewish readers?

_____

_____

_____

3. What must you do if you are going to run the race identified in Hebrews 12:1–2 successfully?

_____

_____

_____

4a. Review the article "Researching Your Own Religious Roots" on pages 48–49, and consider your religious roots. What role has religion played in your family?

_____

_____

_____

4b. How do your religious practices and beliefs differ from your family's? How are they similar?

_____

_____

_____

The history of our families is important to each of us. It may be difficult to accept our varying backgrounds, but God values all the people of the world. God calls each of us to overcome barriers of race, ethnicity, language, and culture. He wants us to reach out to the world with the truth of the gospel.

As you will discover in the next chapter, taking the gospel to a hurting world means more than merely saying, "God bless you. Go in peace." It means getting involved in the world's pain, so we can share and apply the healing message of Jesus Christ.

HEALING THAT HURTS

At the conclusion of the morning worship service, Wanda and George were lamenting to friends about their son, Tommy. "We don't know what to do for Tommy any more," Wanda said. "We raised him right. We sent him to a Christian college. He had been there only two months when he decided to transfer to the state university. But what could we do? He's old enough to make his own decisions."

"Then he joined a fraternity and everything went downhill," George growled angrily. "I know he's partying almost every night. His grades have dropped to *D*s. That boy makes me so mad, I could . . ."

"Be glad you still have a son," a compassionate voice said from behind them. Wanda and George whirled around to see Chris and Bonnie White standing there smiling at them. The surprise on Wanda's and George's faces quickly turned to embarrassment. They knew what the Whites had recently been through.

Bonnie and Chris loved their seventeen-year-old daughter with all their hearts. Marsha was bright, beautiful, talented, and vivacious. She was planning to be a medical missionary some day, and she had already been accepted into the pre-med program at a major university.

One day Chris received an emergency phone call at work. "Mr. White?" a formal, yet nervous sounding voice asked. "This is Chief Reynolds of the police department. We need you to come down to the school right away. There has been an accident."

Chris raced to his car, dove behind the wheel, and stomped the gas pedal to the floor. The vehicle roared out of the parking lot to Marsha's school. His heart sank when he saw Marsha's car and another car at the center of all the commotion. "I'm Chris White!" he yelled to the first uniformed officer he approached. "Chief Reynolds told me there's been an accident. Where's my daughter?"

Chief Reynolds grabbed Chris' shoulder from behind. "You'd better come with me, Mr. White. We need to talk. Your daughter was hit head-on by a drunk driver who was speeding on the wrong side of the road. Mr. White, I'm sorry to have to tell you this, but your daughter is dead."

From the moment Chris heard those awful words, his life was never the same. The next few days blurred into a surrealistic nightmare for him and Bonnie.

"Be thankful you have a son, George." Chris repeated. "You still have a chance to reach Tommy. Don't give up on him. Keep praying for him and encouraging him. Keep building bridges into his world.

"After Marsha's death," Chris continued, "Bonnie and I dropped out of everything. For three months, I could barely function. Then one day a thought kept running through my head, *How long are you going to wallow in self-pity? You aren't mourning for Marsha anymore—you're mourning for yourself.* That day I asked God to give me the strength to get on with life."

"It hasn't been easy," Bonnie added, "but God has helped us through it."

◆ ◆ ◆ ◆ ◆ ◆ ◆ ◆ ◆

If there is anything more heartbreaking than the painful cries of a child, it is the anguished cry of a parent whose child's life has been snatched away. The grief is increased when the reason for the child's death is because of somebody else's foolishness.

Such was the case when Jesus was born. What? You've never heard that side of the story? It's the part of the Christmas story about which few songs are written, but it is a part we can all identify with because, in some measure, we have all known the painful side of life.

WHAT IT MEANS TO BE LIKE JESUS

Jesus indicated that those who follow Him will become like Him (Matt. 10:25). What does it mean to **"be like Jesus"** in today's complex world? Matthew paints eight portraits of what Christlikeness looks like, including:

#2: To Be Like Jesus Means TO ENGAGE THE WORLD'S PAIN

Jesus' entry into human life was fraught with awkward tensions and human dilemmas: a miraculous but nevertheless embarrassing conception, an earthly father who was considering a quiet divorce, an outraged king resorting to infanticide, an early childhood in a strange culture, and a return to a homeland that remained hostile and dangerous. We, too, are all born into some troubles and circumstances. If we want to be like Jesus, we need to face up to the world and remain very much in it, despite all its troubles.

CITY KIDS DIE OVER ADULT MATTERS

In the tragic account in Matthew 2:16–18, we read of an entire village of baby boys being slaughtered, due to the insane rage of a jealous king. The story reminds us that growing numbers of children today die needlessly for the sins of adults.

Like Rachel (v. 18), mothers all over the world, particularly in urban ghettos and developing nations, weep over their dead children. Rachel had lots of experience with tears. Her father tricked her fiancé into marrying her sister and she remained childless for years (Gen. 29:1—30:24). Later, Jeremiah the prophet described her as wailing over the exiled tribes (Jer. 31:15, the passage quoted by Matthew).

The weeping and wailing in Bethlehem must have gone on for days. It could not have been quickly silenced, nor could Rachel's wailing be comforted. The babies of Bethlehem and the people in exile had a common bond: in both cases, innocent people suffered as a result of the proud, ungodly acts of powerful leaders.

continued

continued

Jesus can offer particular comfort to those who grieve the loss of a child. In effect, the babies of Bethlehem died for Him. He must have carried the pain of that throughout His life and onto the cross. It doubtless shaped His special concern for children. And His concerned activity toward them beckons us to find ways to serve children today.

Matthew's retelling of this slaughter is a very significant part of the Christmas story. In a powerful way, it reminds city kids today that they need not die in vain: Jesus lived and died for them, too. ◆

 Matthew 1:18—2:23

¹⁸Now the birth of Jesus Christ was as follows: After His mother Mary was betrothed to Joseph, before they came together, she was found with child of the Holy Spirit. ¹⁹Then Joseph her husband, being a just *man,* and not wanting to make her a public example, was minded to put her away secretly. ²⁰But while he thought about these things, behold, an angel of the Lord appeared to him in a dream, saying, "Joseph, son of David, do not be afraid to take to you Mary your wife, for that which is conceived in her is of the Holy Spirit. ²¹And she will bring forth a Son, and you shall call His name JESUS, for He will save His people from their sins."

²²So all this was done that it might be fulfilled which was spoken by the Lord through the prophet, saying: ²³"Behold, the virgin shall be with child, and bear a Son, and they shall call His name Immanuel," which is translated, "God with us."

²⁴Then Joseph, being aroused from sleep, did as the angel of the Lord commanded him and took to him his wife, ²⁵and did not know her till she had brought forth her firstborn Son. And he called His name JESUS.

CHAPTER 2

¹Now after Jesus was born in Bethlehem of Judea in the days of Herod the king, behold, wise men from the East came to Jerusalem, ²saying, "Where is He who has been born King of the Jews? For we have seen His star in the East and have come to worship Him."

³When Herod the king heard *this,* he was troubled, and all Jerusalem with him. ⁴And when he had gathered all the chief priests and scribes of the people together, he inquired of them where the Christ was to be born.

⁵So they said to him, "In Bethlehem of Judea, for thus it is written by the prophet:

6   'But you, Bethlehem, *in* the land of Judah,
Are not the least among the rulers of
Judah;
For out of you shall come a Ruler
Who will shepherd My people Israel.' "

⁷Then Herod, when he had secretly called the wise men, determined from them what time the star appeared. ⁸And he sent them to Bethlehem and said, "Go and search carefully for the young Child, and when you have found *Him,* bring back word to me, that I may come and worship Him also."

⁹When they heard the king, they departed; and behold, the star which they had seen in the East went before them, till it came and stood over where the young Child was. ¹⁰When they saw the star, they rejoiced with exceedingly great joy. ¹¹And when they had come into the house, they saw the young Child with Mary His mother, and fell down and worshiped Him. And when they had opened their treasures, they presented gifts to Him: gold, frankincense, and myrrh.

¹²Then, being divinely warned in a dream that they should not return to Herod, they departed for their own country another way.

¹³Now when they had departed, behold, an angel of the Lord appeared to Joseph in a dream, saying, "Arise, take the young Child and His mother, flee to Egypt, and stay there until I bring

continued

continued

you word; for Herod will seek the young Child to destroy Him."

¹⁴When he arose, he took the young Child and His mother by night and departed for Egypt, ¹⁵and was there until the death of Herod, that it might be fulfilled which was spoken by the Lord through the prophet, saying, "Out of Egypt I called My Son."

¹⁶Then Herod, when he saw that he was deceived by the wise men, was exceedingly angry; and he sent forth and put to death all the male children who were in Bethlehem and in all its districts, from two years old and under, according to the time which he had determined from the wise men. ¹⁷Then was fulfilled what was spoken by Jeremiah the prophet, saying:

18   "A voice was heard in Ramah,
          Lamentation, weeping, and great
             mourning,

Rachel weeping *for* her children,
Refusing to be comforted,
Because they are no more."

¹⁹Now when Herod was dead, behold, an angel of the Lord appeared in a dream to Joseph in Egypt, ²⁰saying, "Arise, take the young Child and His mother, and go to the land of Israel, for those who sought the young Child's life are dead." ²¹Then he arose, took the young Child and His mother, and came into the land of Israel.

²²But when he heard that Archelaus was reigning over Judea instead of his father Herod, he was afraid to go there. And being warned by God in a dream, he turned aside into the region of Galilee. ²³And he came and dwelt in a city called Nazareth, that it might be fulfilled which was spoken by the prophets, "He shall be called a Nazarene."

---

1. The birth of a baby is usually a joyous, awe-inspiring event. What are some special memories your family has of your birth?

_____

_____

_____

2. What difficult circumstances surrounded your birth?

_____

_____

3. As you read through Jesus' birth narrative in Matthew 1:18—2:23, what are some of the unpleasant details of Jesus' infancy?

_____

_____

_____

4. Why did Herod feel threatened by Jesus?

_____

_____

_____

_____

5a. What key point did Herod misinterpret about Jesus' kingdom?

_____

_____

_____

5b. How do many people make that same mistake today?

_____

_____

_____

——◆ Out of the Cocoon into the World ◆——

Robert and Jill were a happily married Christian couple. They both enjoyed successful careers that allowed them to have a spacious home, nice cars, plenty of nutritious food, and fashionable clothing.

One Sunday morning, their minister invited them to participate in an upcoming missionary trip to Central America. Robert and Jill considered the invitation carefully and decided to sign up.

After two weeks of intensive labor and working directly with people in great need,

Robert and Jill realized how much of the world they had never understood. At home, they read the newspapers and watched television news shows, but the pain and tragedy of any situation presented to them by the media were easy to escape—all they needed to do was put down the paper or change the channel. But when they were dealing with the hurting Central American people face-to-face, Robert and Jill had no means of escape.

◆ ◆ ◆ ◆ ◆ ◆ ◆ ◆ ◆

Robert and Jill are like many of us. It is difficult to fully understand the suffering of others unless we experience it ourselves. We tend to insulate ourselves from the world. God recognized our tendency to withdraw from suffering, so He sent Jesus to show us what it means to sacrifice ourselves for a hurting world. Consequently, Christ calls us to come out of our comfortable "Christian cocoons" and risk taking the gospel to the world around us. ◆

Hebrews 4:14–16

¹⁴Seeing then that we have a great High Priest who has passed through the heavens, Jesus the Son of God, let us hold fast *our* confession. ¹⁵For we do not have a High Priest who cannot sympathize with our weaknesses, but was in all *points* tempted as *we are,* yet without sin. ¹⁶Let us therefore come boldly to the throne of grace, that we may obtain mercy and find grace to help in time of need.

COCOONING

One of the major developments in modern Western society is the phenomenon of "cocooning"—people pulling in, living private lifestyles in which they shut out the world and its concerns. Cocooners have interest only in what touches them, and they set up their environment so that they control what touches them.

Unfortunately, cocooning has subtly invaded the church, contributing to the "pulling in" of Christian faith. It shows up, for instance, in overemphasis on the relationship of the individual to Christ and what He can do for each person, to the neglect of what Christ wants to do among communities of His people, including their corporate responsibilities to each other and the larger society.

The book of Hebrews speaks to the danger of cocooning as it describes Christ's work on our behalf (Heb. 4:14–16):

(1) Christ chose to get involved. *He did not remain in His privileged position with the Father, but "passed through the heavens" (v. 14) to come to earth, becoming poor in order to make us spiritually rich. We can't imagine what that move cost Him.*

(2) Christ faced reality. *He is no stranger to real life. He never walled Himself off from what people go through every day.*

(3) Christ empowers people. *He gives His people sufficient power to deal with life. One rationale for cocooning is the attitude, "When I'm done with work, I'm worn out. I can't be bothered with people's problems. I can hardly manage my own! If anything, I need to be a receiver of grace, not a dispenser of it." Result: the many take comfort, help, and peace from the few who give.*

continued

continued
But verse 16 challenges believers—individually and corporately—to "come boldly to the throne of grace." Why? In order to obtain mercy—a personal need of every individual—and "grace to help *in time of need." Notice: grace* to help. *God's help relieves some of our cares and allows us the freedom and strength to "pass it on" by helping others.* ◆

1. What steps can you take to avoid "Christian cocooning"?

_____

_____

_____

2. How does Christian cocooning indirectly help Satan?

_____

_____

_____

3. What can you do to model Christ by reaching out to others? Check the ideas you may want to pursue.

_____ Work as a counselor in a crisis pregnancy center
_____ Go on a short-term mission trip
_____ Get involved with a Christian service organization
_____ Collect food or clothing to help the needy in my community
_____ Work with a group that builds housing for the homeless

——◆ Being There for People in Pain ◆——

John could not take it any more. Almost every time he entered or exited his downtown office building he was approached by someone asking for a handout. He could hardly pull his car up to one of the busy intersections without seeing another disheveled person standing on the corner holding a handwritten sign reading: OUT OF WORK.

HOMELESS. WILL WORK FOR FOOD.

It wasn't that John was hard-hearted, but sometimes he wished he could escape all the cries for help. Besides, what could he do about the people who were wandering the streets, sleeping in cardboard boxes, and scrounging through garbage cans for food?

Then, one day while John was on his lunch break, a young woman with two small children approached him. "Excuse me, sir," she pleaded. "My husband is gone and my daughter is very sick. I don't have a car, and I can't afford a cab. Could you please help us to get to the hospital?"

John began to make an excuse about not having enough time to help her, when suddenly he caught a glimpse of the desperate look in the eyes of the little girl. She was about the age of his only daughter. *What if something ever happened to him, and it was his child who needed help?* John wondered.

John left his lunch on a park bench and led the woman and her children to his car. When they arrived at the emergency room, John made sure the child would receive the care she needed. The woman expressed her gratitude, and John hurried back to his car. He was going to be late getting back to the office, but he didn't care. As John drove back to his office, he realized that he felt good about himself for the first time in a long while. He realized that he could do something to help somebody less fortunate than himself.

◆ ◆ ◆ ◆ ◆ ◆ ◆ ◆ ◆

Often the pain a hurting person experiences is more than a physical ailment. It is a deep-seated sense of rejection and a feeling of being unimportant. Sometimes just knowing that someone else cares may be all the healing a person needs. Regardless of the physical need, everyone needs to know about the One who can not only heal the body, but also heal the soul. ◆

THE HEMORRHAGING WOMAN

For twelve years the woman in Matthew 9:20–22 had sought a cure for her condition. Perhaps worse than the drain on her physical strength and finances was the stigma of uncleanness. Jews considered women ritually unclean during menstruation, and whoever touched a menstruating woman was made unclean until evening. If a woman experienced bleeding other than at her normal menses, she was considered unclean until the bleeding stopped (Lev. 15:19–27). That meant exclusion from participating in the life and worship of the community.

Scripture is silent on the source of this woman's livelihood. Perhaps she lived off an inheritance, or perhaps she was divorced and her dowry had been returned to her. Whatever her means of support, it was gone. Jesus was her last hope.

So she approached Him, breaking a rule that made it an unclean person's responsibility to keep away from others. In desperation, she reached out and touched Jesus.

Perceiving that power had gone out from Him, Jesus sought her out. Perhaps as she explained her disease the crowd backed away, not wanting to contaminate themselves. But Jesus didn't withdraw. Rather He drew her to Him with the affectionate term "daughter" and sent her away in peace, healed at last.

Who are the "untouchables" in your world? Who is desperately trying to reach out for help? How can you respond to their needs with Christlikeness?

 Matthew 9:18–22

18While He spoke these things to them, behold, a ruler came and worshiped Him, saying, "My daughter has just died, but come and lay Your hand on her and she will live." 19So Jesus arose and followed him, and so *did* His disciples. 20And suddenly, a woman who had a flow of blood for twelve years came from behind and touched the hem of His garment. 21For she said to herself, "If only I may touch His garment, I shall be made well." 22But Jesus turned around, and when He saw her He said, "Be of good cheer, daughter; your faith has made you well." And the woman was made well from that hour.

1. What personal losses have caused you grief?

_____ Death of a loved one
_____ Divorce or separation
_____ Loss of purpose or a long-term goal
_____ Loss of youth or innocence
_____ Leaving home or moving to a distant location

2a. Some losses are realized over a period of time. This was the case with the hemorrhaging woman. What were her needs?

Physical _____

Spiritual _____

Financial _____

2b. How did Jesus meet each of those needs?

_____

_____

_____

3. How do Jesus' dealings with this woman encourage you to do something to help meet the needs of others?

_____

_____

_____

——◆ Hope for a World Afflicted by Evil ◆——

People have been suffering through painful circumstances since the beginning of time. Many people have questioned why God allows so much pain in His world if He is good and loving. Unfortunately, all the logical answers to this question fall on deaf ears when the pain is racking your body or that of someone you love.

The one thing you can be certain of is that your pain has not gone unnoticed by God. He knows what you are going through and He cares. Even though everything seems to be crashing down around you, God has promised that He will never allow you to be tempted or tested more than you can bear (1 Cor. 10:13). He is aware of what you are going through, and He has already placed limits on how much the pain can affect you. In the meantime, He will give you the strength to cope with pain.

Elizabeth Skoglund, an author and professional Christian counselor, discovered this while visiting a small, primitive town in Mexico where she contracted a severe case of amoebic dysentery. With her body quaking from pain and fever and being far removed from any modern medical facilities, she did the only thing she could—she prayed. Elizabeth recalls:

As I lay in bed that afternoon I calmly asked God to heal me. A logical request since I firmly believed that God's purposes for my life were still alive and real and that they required health. The result was a shaky but increasing return to physical well-being by the evening. I do not believe that God unfailingly answers our prayers for healing with an answer of yes. Sometimes He says no or wait. Or, He chooses to give partial help. But at a time when I was without usable medical attention, God undertook to do the whole job Himself, an experience that was very bolstering to my faith in future days. God had provided for my needs as my life was centered in His will. He had not prevented the illness nor did He eliminate illness on future trips. But He did provide for my physical needs. He helped me to more than cope. He healed when that was necessary.

GOD RESTRAINS EVIL

The presence of pain, suffering, and evil in the world causes some people to wonder whether a good God exists, and if He does, why He doesn't put an end to it if He can. John's vision of a beast rising up out of the sea (Rev. 13:1) and causing great havoc in the world does not explain why there is evil, but it does sound an important note of encouragement: the evils of the world happen only by "permission" and those that do occur have precise limits imposed on them by God. Notice that the beast "was given authority to continue for forty-two months" (Rev. 13:5, emphasis added).

Clearly, God has placed restraints on evil. We have not and will not experience the full onslaught of pain and suffering that could be delivered. This restraining work of God can be seen in several incidents in the Old Testament:

- Adam and Eve (Gen. 3:22–24). After Adam and Eve sinned, God sent them out of the garden and sealed it off. According to Genesis, this was not a matter of retaliation by God but a protection from the possibility of eating from the tree of life and being separated from Him forever.
- The Flood (Gen. 6:5–8). When evil had corrupted the entire world, God acted with "severe mercy" by sending the flood. This restricted evil and made possible a second start for the earth.
- The Tower of Babel (Gen. 11:1–9). Again, widespread evil threatened to consume the creation. God intervened by confusing the languages of the peoples to limit their

continued

continued

collusion in wickedness. This was a case of God preserving sinful humanity from itself.

• Job (Job 1:6—2:10). *Satan wanted to prove to God that Job's faithfulness was merely the result of God blessing him. So God granted Satan limited permission to inflict suffering.*

John was writing to believers to help them maintain a realistic view of good and evil in the midst of intense persecution. Today, as we watch televised reports of death and disaster around the world and as we experience pain and suffering in our own families and among our neighbors and associates, we too need to maintain a godly perspective. God has placed limits on evil. The very fact that we have a distaste for it reflects that we do indeed bear God's image as His creatures. ◆

Revelation 13:1–18

[1]Then I stood on the sand of the sea. And I saw a beast rising up out of the sea, having seven heads and ten horns, and on his horns ten crowns, and on his heads a blasphemous name. [2]Now the beast which I saw was like a leopard, his feet were like *the feet of* a bear, and his mouth like the mouth of a lion. The dragon gave him his power, his throne, and great authority. [3]And *I saw* one of his heads as if it had been mortally wounded, and his deadly wound was healed. And all the world marveled and followed the beast. [4]So they worshiped the dragon who gave authority to the beast; and they worshiped the beast, saying, "Who *is* like the beast? Who is able to make war with him?"

[5]And he was given a mouth speaking great things and blasphemies, and he was given authority to continue for forty-two months. [6]Then he opened his mouth in blasphemy against God, to blaspheme His name, His tabernacle, and those who dwell in heaven. [7]It was granted to him to make war with the saints and to overcome them. And authority was given him over every tribe, tongue, and nation. [8]All who dwell on the earth will worship him, whose names have not been written in the Book of Life of the Lamb slain from the foundation of the world.

[9]If anyone has an ear, let him hear. [10]He who leads into captivity shall go into captivity; he who kills with the sword must be killed with the sword. Here is the patience and the faith of the saints.

[11]Then I saw another beast coming up out of the earth, and he had two horns like a lamb and spoke like a dragon. [12]And he exercises all the authority of the first beast in his presence, and causes the earth and those who dwell in it to worship the first beast, whose deadly wound was healed. [13]He performs great signs, so that he even makes fire come down from heaven on the earth in the sight of men. [14]And he deceives those who dwell on the earth by those signs which he was granted to do in the sight of the beast, telling those who dwell on the earth to make an image to the beast who was wounded by the sword and lived. [15]He was granted *power* to give breath to the image of the beast, that the image of the beast should both speak and cause as many as would not worship the image of the beast to be killed. [16]He causes all, both small and great, rich and poor, free and slave, to receive a mark on their right hand or on their foreheads, [17]and that no one may buy or sell except one who has the mark or the name of the beast, or the number of his name.

[18]Here is wisdom. Let him who has understanding calculate the number of the beast, for it is the number of a man: His number *is* 666.

1. Describe a time in your life when God relieved your pain.

_____

_____

_____

2. Many people are reluctant to read the book of Revelation. This book is not meant to scare believers, but to encourage them. What encouragement can you find in Revelation 13:1–18?

_____

_____

_____

3. How is God helping you cope with a painful or difficult situation in your life right now?

_____

_____

_____

♦ ♦ ♦ ♦ ♦ ♦ ♦ ♦ ♦

You won't have to look very far to find hurting people in your world—they are all around you. Jesus loves every one of those hurting people. He gave His life for them, just as He gave it for you. Now, you are called to take Christ's message of love, hope, and salvation to your world.

You really have only two alternatives when you think about the hurting people around you. You can close your eyes and pretend the problems don't exist, or you can obey Jesus by reaching out to those in pain.

The needs of the hurting people all around you are indeed daunting. But the task of reaching out to others becomes more manageable if you just reach out to one person at a time. All you have to do is commit yourself to doing so.

CLEAR COMMITMENT

Are you afraid of making commitments? Many people are, you know. With the ever-increasing divorce rate, a transient society, and the lack of job security, almost nothing seems like a reliable investment of our time, energy, and emotions.

Even Christians experience this fear of commitment. Marriages between Christians sometimes end in divorce; Christians still lose their jobs no matter how hard they work; and Christians sometimes feel insecure about the future. Many believers have even refused to join a church. Their commitment to Christ is conditional, and their prayers sound somewhat like this:

Oh, God, I will serve You if You will show me everything You plan to get me into, and if it's not painful, and if I won't suffer, nor incur any cost, threat, or risk—then, I will serve You. Now, Lord, please reveal Your will to me.

Unquestionably, such fickleness is not the stuff faith is made of. If you really want to see a picture of faith, take a look at John the Baptist. He believed in Jesus long before it was popular to do so. John would not back away from his commitment—regardless of the cost—and Jesus would not back away from John the Baptist.

WHAT IT MEANS TO BE LIKE JESUS

*Jesus indicated that those who follow Him will become like Him (Matt. 10:25). What does it mean to **"be like Jesus"** in today's complex world? Matthew paints eight portraits of what Christlikeness looks like, including:*

#3: To Be Like Jesus Means TO COMMIT OURSELVES TO OTHER BELIEVERS

John the Baptist was not your average individual. He was an unexpected child. He lived in the wilderness—the "other side of the tracks" for that day. He wore strange clothing and ate strange food. He was pugnacious, even offensive at times. Yet he helped launch Jesus' career. In return, Jesus had nothing but praise for him. If we want to be like Jesus, we must not pick and choose our brothers and sisters in God's family. We need to embrace other believers and demonstrate our unity in Christ, no matter how awkward or inconvenient.

Matthew 3:1–17

¹In those days John the Baptist came preaching in the wilderness of Judea, ²and saying, "Repent, for the kingdom of heaven is at hand!" ³For this is he who was spoken of by the prophet Isaiah, saying:

"The voice of one crying in the wilderness:
'Prepare the way of the LORD;
Make His paths straight.' "

continued

continued

⁴Now John himself was clothed in camel's hair, with a leather belt around his waist; and his food was locusts and wild honey. ⁵Then Jerusalem, all Judea, and all the region around the Jordan went out to him ⁶and were baptized by him in the Jordan, confessing their sins.

⁷But when he saw many of the Pharisees and Sadducees coming to his baptism, he said to them, "Brood of vipers! Who warned you to flee from the wrath to come? ⁸Therefore bear fruits worthy of repentance, ⁹and do not think to say to yourselves, 'We have Abraham as *our* father.' For I say to you that God is able to raise up children to Abraham from these stones. ¹⁰And even now the ax is laid to the root of the trees. Therefore every tree which does not bear good fruit is cut down and thrown into the fire. ¹¹I indeed baptize you with water unto repentance, but He who is coming after me is mightier than I, whose sandals I am not worthy to carry. He will baptize you with the Holy Spirit and fire. ¹²His winnowing fan *is* in His hand, and He will thoroughly clean out His threshing floor, and gather His wheat into the barn; but He will burn up the chaff with unquenchable fire."

¹³Then Jesus came from Galilee to John at the Jordan to be baptized by him. ¹⁴And John *tried to* prevent Him, saying, "I need to be baptized by You, and are You coming to me?"

¹⁵But Jesus answered and said to him, "Permit *it to be so* now, for thus it is fitting for us to fulfill all righteousness." Then he allowed Him.

¹⁶When He had been baptized, Jesus came up immediately from the water; and behold, the heavens were opened to Him, and He saw the Spirit of God descending like a dove and alighting upon Him. ¹⁷And suddenly a voice *came* from heaven, saying, "This is My beloved Son, in whom I am well pleased."

1. Jesus reached out to John the Baptist, despite John's strange appearance and behavior. What does that tell you about some of the "strange" people you may encounter?

_____

_____

_____

2. Why do you think people who walk closely with God sometimes seem out-of-sync with the rest of the world?

_____

_____

3. John's lifestyle and message were radically different from other preachers and religious leaders of his day. List some of the things about him or his message that set him apart from the crowd.

_____

_____

_____

4. Why do you think John was reluctant to baptize Jesus?

_____

_____

5. Why was it appropriate, even necessary, for John the Baptist to baptize Jesus?

_____

_____

———◆ What Makes You a Christian? ◆———

Pretend that you are unable to tell people that you are a Christian. The only way others can know this is through your behavior and your actions. Why would anyone call you a Christian? Check the answers that might apply to you.

People know I am a Christian because:

_____ I wear a cross around my neck.   _____ I give money to the poor.
_____ I go to church regularly.   _____ I love others as I love myself.
_____ I pray before meals.   _____ I treat people fairly.

It may surprise you to learn that Jesus never indicated that His disciples would be differentiated by their dress or their spiritual demeanor. To Christ, the telltale signs of His followers run much deeper than superficial fluff.

THE HALLMARK OF LOVE

A key test of our commitment to Christ is our love for other believers (John 13:31–35). It is not just our words that express our love, but our attitudes and actions as well. Jesus did not say that others would know we are His disciples by what we say, or how we dress, or what we know, or the label of our denomination. He said, "as I have loved you" (v. 34). Shortly afterward, He laid down His life for those first believers.

 John 13:1–17, 31–35

¹Now before the Feast of the Passover, when Jesus knew that His hour had come that He should depart from this world to the Father, having loved His own who were in the world, He loved them to the end. ²And supper being ended, the devil having already put it into the heart of Judas Iscariot, Simon's *son*, to betray Him, ³Jesus, knowing that the Father had given all things into His hands, and that He had come from God and was going to God, ⁴rose from supper and laid aside His garments, took a towel and

continued

continued

girded Himself. ⁵After that, He poured water into a basin and began to wash the disciples' feet, and to wipe *them* with the towel with which He was girded. ⁶Then He came to Simon Peter. And *Peter* said to Him, "Lord, are You washing my feet?"

⁷Jesus answered and said to him, "What I am doing you do not understand now, but you will know after this."

⁸Peter said to Him, "You shall never wash my feet!" Jesus answered him, "If I do not wash you, you have no part with Me."

⁹Simon Peter said to Him, "Lord, not my feet only, but also *my* hands and *my* head!"

¹⁰Jesus said to him, "He who is bathed needs only to wash *his* feet, but is completely clean; and you are clean, but not all of you." ¹¹For He knew who would betray Him; therefore He said, "You are not all clean."

¹²So when He had washed their feet, taken His garments, and sat down again, He said to them, "Do you know what I have done to you? ¹³You call Me Teacher and Lord, and you say well, for *so* I am. ¹⁴If I then, *your* Lord and Teacher, have washed your feet, you also ought to wash one another's feet. ¹⁵For I have given you an example, that you should do as I have done to you. ¹⁶Most assuredly, I say to you, a servant is not greater than his master; nor is he who is sent greater than he who sent him. ¹⁷If you know these things, blessed are you if you do them.

. . .

³¹So, when he had gone out, Jesus said, "Now the Son of Man is glorified, and God is glorified in Him. ³²If God is glorified in Him, God will also glorify Him in Himself, and glorify Him immediately. ³³Little children, I shall be with you a little while longer. You will seek Me; and as I said to the Jews, 'Where I am going, you cannot come,' so now I say to you. ³⁴A new commandment I give to you, that you love one another; as I have loved you, that you also love one another. ³⁵By this all will know that you are My disciples, if you have love for one another."

1. What lesson was Jesus teaching when He washed the disciples' feet?

_____

_____

_____

_____

2. Why did Peter object to Jesus' washing his feet (John 13:6–10)?

_____

_____

_____

_____

3. How are you trying to follow Jesus' example of humble, servant-leadership? (For instance: I am willing to do the unpleasant jobs at work; I am not afraid to get my hands dirty.)

_____

_____

_____

4. Jesus said His disciples could be detected by their love for one another (John 13:34–35). How can you begin showing Christ's love toward others?

_____

_____

_____

———◆ Reclaiming the Rejected ◆———

Jeff and Steve were rummaging around in the attic of their parents' home. Their mom and dad had died recently, and the brothers had the dubious task of sifting through their parents' possessions, deciding what should be kept and what could be thrown away. As they worked in the dusty attic, tears occasionally trickled down their faces when they discovered boxes filled with old photographs and other memorabilia.

Suddenly, Steve's eye caught a glimpse of a silver object sticking out beneath a stack of old magazines and newspapers. It looked to Steve as though the object was part of an old horn. Steve picked through the debris and carefully pulled the tarnished object from the pile of rubble. Sure enough, it was an old French horn that someone had carelessly cast aside years ago.

"What are you going to do with that piece of junk?" Jeff asked, as Steve held the horn up to the light.

"Are you kidding? Don't you recognize this horn?" Steve answered. "It was Dad's horn when he was just a boy. He used to play it in the junior high band. Look, it's still in good shape. With some work, I think I could fix this thing up so it will play."

"Humph," Jeff grunted. "It looks like more work than it's worth, if you ask me. Come on, let's get out of this dust bowl."

A few weeks later, Steve stopped by Jeff's house after work. "Look at this baby!" Steve exclaimed as he pulled the gleaming French horn from its case. "I've been working on it every chance I get. I replaced the broken valves, shined everything inside and out, bought a new mouthpiece, and even found a case for it. Now, listen to this!"

Steve put the mouthpiece of the restored French horn to his lips and began to blow, first softly, then with more intensity. Jeff stared in amazement. He could hardly believe what he was hearing! Coming from the old horn were some of the most beautiful sounds he had ever heard—lush, rich, mellow tones that can't be mimicked by modern horns. "I can't believe it!" Jeff cried. "You've taken that old thing and made it into a beautiful instrument."

"Naw, the beauty was already there," Steve replied. "It had just been covered with dirt. All I did was repair a few broken pieces and polish it up. It's like a brand new instrument—maybe better. The guy down at the music store offered me fifteen hundred dollars for it."

"What? And you didn't take it?" Jeff asked.

"No way. This was Dad's horn. To me, it's worth a lot more than any amount of money."

◆ ◆ ◆ ◆ ◆ ◆ ◆ ◆ ◆

In a way, your life is much like that refurbished French horn. You are valuable not because of who you are or what you can do, but because of whose *you are. You have value because God created you. There has never been—and never will be—another of God's masterpieces just like you!*

Maybe God has had to dust you off, clean some dirt out of your life, straighten some crooked parts, and replace or repair some broken pieces. But in the process, He has restored your original beauty. And God has you—yes, you—in His family album. Take a look! ◆

GOD'S FAMILY ALBUM

The names that Peter calls believers (1 Peter 2:9–10) are important because they reveal our identity. We know *who* we are because we know *whose* we are: we belong to God. We have received His call, mercy, and claim on our lives. As a result, we can commit ourselves to others and work with them to achieve common goals.

Peter draws on the Exodus account for his language here: "I . . . brought you [out of Egypt] to Myself . . . You shall be to Me a kingdom of priests" (Ex. 19:4–6). God first identified with and redeemed the people of Israel, then He made covenant agreements with them. Likewise for us, first God's grace secures our identity, then our commitment to His service.

Our modern culture tears at that sense of identity and security. If we want to effect change and serve others, we need to know *whose* we are and why. Do you? Can you find yourself in God's family portrait framed in this passage?

---

 1 Peter 2:4–10

[4]Coming to Him *as to* a living stone, rejected indeed by men, but chosen by God *and* precious, [5]you also, as living stones, are being built up a spiritual house, a holy priesthood, to offer up spiritual sacrifices acceptable to God through Jesus Christ. [6]Therefore it is also contained in the Scripture,

> "Behold, I lay in Zion
> A chief cornerstone, elect, precious,
> And he who believes on Him will by no
> means be put to shame."

[7]Therefore, to you who believe, *He is* precious; but to those who are disobedient,

> "The stone which the builders rejected
> Has become the chief cornerstone,"

[8]and

> "A stone of stumbling
> And a rock of offense."

They stumble, being disobedient to the word, to which they also were appointed.

continued

> *continued*
> ⁹But you *are* a chosen generation, a royal priesthood, a holy nation, His own special people, that you may proclaim the praises of Him who called you out of darkness into His marvelous light; ¹⁰who once *were* not a people but *are* now the people of God, who had not obtained mercy but now have obtained mercy.

1. Not long ago, a Vincent van Gogh painting sold for over forty-two million dollars. The painting is lovely, but you could probably purchase a reproduction of the piece for less than fifty dollars. What makes the van Gogh painting so valuable?

_____ The artist had only one ear
_____ The painting was an original creation
_____ Inflation
_____ The immeasurable skill of the master artist who created it

2. According to Scripture, you possess immense value. In light of 1 Peter 2:4–10, how can you have a healthy self-concept without slipping into sinful pride?

_____

_____

_____

3. What is Peter talking about in verses 7 and 8, when he refers to the stone which the builders rejected, which then became the chief cornerstone?

_____

_____

_____

4. In what ways were you rejected or cast off before you trusted Christ as your Savior?

_____

_____

_____

5. How has God reclaimed that which the world rejected or cast off in your life?

_____

_____

_____

◆ Friends in Low Places ◆

Pressure can bring out the best in people. During the floods in 1993 that took over the midwestern United States, people of every background and social status pitched in to build walls of sandbags in an effort to keep the floodwaters out of their towns.

Complete strangers worked side-by-side to achieve a common goal. Some won the battle; others failed. But all found the threat of death and the potential destruction of their dreams to be a powerful common denominator.

Something similar must have happened the day Jesus went before Pontius Pilate. The crucifixion of Christ brought together an unusual collection of Jesus' friends. This happens today wherever people gather in the name of Jesus.

A REMARKABLE COALITION

We live in a world where groups of people tend to exclude others rather than include them. Seldom do people from vastly different backgrounds band together, unless it's to fight a common enemy. Distinctions such as race, money, position, language, and gender often keep people from cooperating with each other.

But for those who followed Jesus, divisive walls began to break down. As a result of His influence, people who were far apart socially began to come together for the benefit of others.

Such was the case at Jesus' burial. His death brought about a surprising coalition: two men who were prominent Jewish leaders, and two women, one who had been delivered from demon possession and the other an obscure mother (Luke 23:50–56). Who were these people?

Joseph of Arimathea *was a wealthy community leader and a member of the Jewish council. He had access to Pilate and gained permission to take away Jesus' body. He helped prepare the body for burial and deliver it to his own tomb (vv. 50–53; Matt. 27:57–60; Mark 15:42–46).*

Nicodemus *was also a member of the council (John 3:1–2). He challenged some of the accusations against Jesus (7:50–51). After the Lord's death, he brought nearly 100 pounds of embalming supplies (19:39–42).*

Mary Magdalene *came from Galilee. She had been demon-possessed before following Jesus (Luke 8:2). Along with other women she observed the tragic*

continued

continued

ordeal of the crucifixion (23:49). After Joseph retrieved the body, she helped with the embalming (v. 56). Later, after Jesus' resurrection, she helped spread the amazing news that He was alive (24:10).

Mary of Galilee *was the mother of James and Joses (Mark 15:40). Little else is known about her, but she played enough of a part in the*

burial coalition to have her participation recorded in Scripture.

Does your faith connect you with people different from yourself? Believers often have more in common with other believers than they do with family, friends, or coworkers. That fact can sometimes be just the bit of evidence needed to make the faith attractive to its worst critics. ◆

 Luke 23:50–56

⁵⁰Now behold, *there was* a man named Joseph, a council member, a good and just man. ⁵¹He had not consented to their decision and deed. *He was* from Arimathea, a city of the Jews, who himself was also waiting for the kingdom of God. ⁵²This man went to Pilate and asked for the body of Jesus. ⁵³Then he took it down, wrapped it in linen, and laid it in a tomb *that was* hewn out of the rock, where no one had ever lain before.

⁵⁴That day was the Preparation, and the Sabbath drew near.

⁵⁵And the women who had come with Him from Galilee followed after, and they observed the tomb and how His body was laid. ⁵⁶Then they returned and prepared spices and fragrant oils. And they rested on the Sabbath according to the commandment.

1. Why was Joseph of Arimathea's request to bury Jesus' body a risky venture?

_____

_____

2. Although the Galilean women who followed Jesus did not do much for Christ, they did what they could. List several ways in which they showed their commitment to Christ. What reward did they receive for their efforts?

_____

_____

3. Sometimes you may feel as though your talents, time, or financial resources are so limited that you have little to give. The women at the cross remind us that what you cannot do for Christ is irrelevant; the real issue is what you can do. What are some practical ways you can show evidence of your commitment to Christ this week?

_____

_____

_____

◆ Open Hands or Sticky Fingers ◆

Wendy and Doug were embarrassed. They had traveled to Jamaica to help repair a church there and to be a source of encouragement to the local believers. Wendy and Doug had heard that their hosts, Pastor Johnson and his family, were living in abject poverty. Consequently, the Americans had been reluctant to accept their hosts' invitation to share a meal at the pastor's home. They didn't want to insult their hosts though, so they accepted the invitation.

Now, as they sat around Pastor Johnson's table, the pastor's wife kept bringing out more food and placing it before them. In spite of their own lack of food, money, indoor plumbing, and a host of other "necessities," Pastor Johnson and his family had gone to great lengths to put on the best meal they could

for their American guests.

"But we came here to help you," Wendy had protested as she helped Mrs. Johnson bring in the meal from the outdoor kitchen, which was totally devoid of the modern, appliance-equipped space Wendy was accustomed to back home. "We don't expect you to be serving us; we came here to serve you."

"No problem," Mrs. Johnson replied with a wide grin. "Eat up. It's good for you."

Throughout the entire meal, Wendy and Doug were amazed at the generosity of the Jamaican couple. Later that night, as the American couple spread out their sleeping bags on the wire bed springs in the Johnson's bedroom, Doug was still overwhelmed. "Think about it," he said to Wendy. "This family, which has so little of the world's goods, gave us

so much. Yet back home, we who have so much are willing to give so little to others. It seems backwards, doesn't it?"

"Yes, it does, Doug," Wendy said softly.

◆ ◆ ◆ ◆ ◆ ◆ ◆ ◆ ◆

The Jamaican pastor and his family, like the early Christians, were not stingy when it came to money and material goods. Their love for Christ spilled over to a love for each other, a love that was manifested in spontaneous acts of kindness, compassion, and generosity toward fellow believers.

God wants each of us to have a similar spirit of giving. Our generosity should not be a show to gain the applause or approval of other people, but a genuine expression of love and compassion in response to God's great gifts. He wants us to discover the joy of giving generously and blessing others as He has blessed us. ◆

SHARING THINGS IN COMMON

The first Christians were extraordinarily generous. In fact, "they had all things in common" (Acts 4:32–35), an ideal that pure communism advocated but never achieved. So were these first believers in some sense communists?

No. In the first place, they were not setting up an economic system here, but simply responding to each other with gracious, Christlike compassion. Such behavior was one powerful result of the outpouring of the Spirit (Acts 2:1–4). Unfortunately, not all New Testament believers demonstrated that kind

of concern (Acts 5:1–11; 1 Cor. 6:8; James 4:1–2).

Furthermore, Scripture never mandates an equal distribution of goods, nor does it call for the elimination of property or ownership. Acts 4:32–35 (along with Acts 2:44–45) is a historical account, not a doctrinal treatise. It documents the work of God in building the early church.

In that day, as in ours, there were both rich and poor Christians (2 Cor. 8:2; 1 Tim. 6:17–19). And when the New Testament does address issues such as wealth, care for the poor, work, equality, widows, slaves, and public justice, it inevitably calls believers to compassion and generosity; but not to asceti-

continued

continued

cism, the idea that one can become more godly through self-denial and renouncing worldly wealth. In fact, Paul warns against that (Col. 2:18–23). The Bible condemns the love of wealth, not its possession, as a root of all kinds of evil (1 Tim. 6:9–10).

Reading about these early Christians, modern believers are challenged to consider: Do we, with our much higher standard of living, show the same commitment to generosity as these believers? If we, too, are filled with the Spirit of Christ, then we ought to respond to the needs of people with the love of Christ.

ANANIAS AND SAPPHIRA— PLAYING GAMES WITH GOD

The dramatic account of Ananias and Sapphira (Acts 5:1–11) immediately after the mention of Barnabas (4:36–37) draws a stark contrast between two kinds of people. On the one hand, Barnabas serves as a positive model of sincere faith, as evidenced by his open-handed generosity. On the other hand, Ananias and Sapphira serve as negative models.

Externally, they appeared the same. Like Barnabas, they sold land and brought money to the church, where they "laid it at the apostles' feet" (4:37; 5:2). But internally, they had a radically different commitment.

The sins that Peter named—lying to the Holy Spirit (5:3) and testing the Spirit (5:9)—indicate that they were playing games with God. Peter noted that the source of their deception was Satan. As the ultimate liar (John 8:44), Satan had filled their hearts with lies, in contrast to the Holy Spirit, who fills the heart with truth (14:16–17; Eph. 5:6–21). And like Israel, they were testing the Spirit (1 Cor. 10:1–13), testing the limits of what He would permit, trying to see how much they could get away with.

God dealt severely with this couple by making an example of them. As a result, fear came upon the church (Acts 5:5, 11)—not a cringing fear of dread, but a heightened respect for God's holiness, His moral purity. The incident still stands as a bold warning to believers today about relating to God. No one is perfect, and God forgives. But when given a chance to confess the truth, it's important to confess the truth, not lie as they did.

 Acts 4:32—5:11

32Now the multitude of those who believed were of one heart and one soul; neither did anyone say that any of the things he possessed was his own, but they had all things in common. 33And with great power the apostles gave witness to the resurrection of the Lord Jesus. And great grace was upon them all. 34Nor was there anyone among them who lacked; for all who were possessors of lands or houses sold them, and brought the proceeds of the things that were sold, 35and laid *them* at the apostles' feet; and they distributed to each as anyone had need.

36And Joses, who was also named Barnabas by the apostles (which is translated Son of Encouragement), a Levite of the country of Cyprus, 37having land, sold *it,* and brought the money and laid *it* at the apostles' feet.

CHAPTER 5

1But a certain man named Ananias, with Sapphira his wife, sold a possession. 2And he kept back *part* of the proceeds, his wife also being aware *of it,* and brought a certain part and laid *it* at the apostles' feet. 3But Peter said, "Ananias, why has Satan filled your heart to lie to the Holy Spirit and keep back *part* of the price of the land for yourself? 4While it remained, was it not your

continued

continued

own? And after it was sold, was it not in your own control? Why have you conceived this thing in your heart? You have not lied to men but to God."

⁵Then Ananias, hearing these words, fell down and breathed his last. So great fear came upon all those who heard these things. ⁶And the young men arose and wrapped him up, carried *him* out, and buried *him.*

⁷Now it was about three hours later when his wife came in, not knowing what had happened.

⁸And Peter answered her, "Tell me whether you sold the land for so much?"

She said, "Yes, for so much."

⁹Then Peter said to her, "How is it that you have agreed together to test the Spirit of the Lord? Look, the feet of those who have buried your husband *are* at the door, and they will carry you out." ¹⁰Then immediately she fell down at his feet and breathed her last. And the young men came in and found her dead, and carrying *her* out, buried *her* by her husband. ¹¹So great fear came upon all the church and upon all who heard these things.

1. Generosity is not always measurable in dollars and cents. What are some other standards by which you measure generosity?

_____

_____

_____

_____

2. In Acts 4:32—5:11, Barnabas sold his property and gave the proceeds to the apostles. Ananias and Sapphira sold some of their possessions and also gave money to the apostles. Yet Barnabas was blessed for his actions while Ananias and Sapphira died because of their actions. What made the difference?

_____

_____

_____

3. How can you be more like Barnabas in expressing your generosity?

_____

_____

_____

_____

Your commitment to Christ impacts every area of your life. It involves your relationship with your marriage partner (or your attitudes toward marriage or singleness), as well as your relationships with friends, family, and coworkers. It involves what you do with your time, money, and other resources. Jesus didn't call you to simply accept a creed or a doctrine; He has called you to commit yourself to being a believer who follows Him, learns from Him, and then takes His message to the world.

But God never intended for you to function as a spiritual loner. He wants you to have fellow believers to whom you can turn for fellowship, instruction, and encouragement; He also expects you to be there for others. Jesus said the world will recognize that you belong to Him, not simply by your words, but by your love. And true love requires commitment.

Without commitment, Christlike love is impossible. When commitment and love are lacking, we are more susceptible to temptation, which can lead to sin.

It's important to understand that temptation itself is not sin. You will never be able to absolutely avoid being tempted. The key is to learn how to overcome temptation.

TURN AWAY FROM TEMPTATION

There are some Christians who believe that once you reach a certain plateau in your spiritual experience, you no longer have to deal with temptation. However, no new state of Christian living is going to prevent you from being tempted.

But temptation is not sin! You can be tempted intensely and frequently without sinning. You do not sin until you yield to temptation. Many Christians carry around mounds of guilt simply because they are experiencing temptation. Somehow, they have acquired the false notion that being tempted is equal to committing the sin.

You cannot avoid the initial thoughts that pop into your mind any more than you can control the sudden, tempting commercial that bursts onto your television screen during an otherwise inoffensive program. You can, however, choose to put those tempting thoughts out of your mind, just as you can choose to change the channel when offensive material suddenly dances across your television screen.

The question is often asked, "When does temptation turn into sin?" For example: You do an exceptional job at work; when does your sense of accomplishment turn into sinful pride? Or, consider this: You observe an attractive person walking into a room; when do you cease admiring one of God's creations and become preoccupied with inappropriate thoughts?

Billy Graham used to say that it is not the first look that is sinful, but it is the second look, and the third . . . In other words, sin begins whenever we dwell on a tempting situation or permit ourselves to remain in a compromising situation. Then, almost imperceptibly, temptation leads to sin.

Although temptation affects all of us, God has promised that He will help us overcome temptation. God may allow temptations to come our way, but He is never out of touch with our circumstances. He knows what we are going through and will give us the help we need to overcome temptation. It is important that we realize two vital truths:

1. It is not a sin to experience temptation.
2. We will be tempted throughout life.

The apostle Paul was tempted. Devout Christians throughout history have been tempted. Even Christ was tempted by Satan. Jesus is different, though, because He showed us that it is possible to be tempted and not sin.

When we allow Jesus to work in and through our lives, it is possible to endure temptation without giving in to sin. The first step to overcoming temptation is to admit that we are vulnerable to it.

Matthew 4:1–11

¹Then Jesus was led up by the Spirit into the wilderness to be tempted by the devil. ²And when He had fasted forty days and forty nights, afterward He was hungry. ³Now when the tempter came to Him, he said, "If You are the Son of God, command that these stones become bread."

⁴But He answered and said, "It is written, 'Man shall not live by bread alone, but by every word that proceeds from the mouth of God.'"

⁵Then the devil took Him up into the holy city, set Him on the pinnacle of the temple, ⁶and

continued

continued
said to Him, "If You are the Son of God, throw Yourself down. For it is written:

> 'He shall give His angels charge over you,'

and,

> 'In *their* hands they shall bear you up,
> Lest you dash your foot against a stone.' "

7Jesus said to him, "It is written again, 'You shall not tempt the LORD your God.' "

8Again, the devil took Him up on an exceedingly high mountain, and showed Him all the kingdoms of the world and their glory. 9And he said to Him, "All these things I will give You if You will fall down and worship me."

10Then Jesus said to him, "Away with you, Satan! For it is written, 'You shall worship the LORD your God, and Him only you shall serve.' "

11Then the devil left Him, and behold, angels came and ministered to Him.

WHAT IT MEANS TO BE LIKE JESUS

*Jesus indicated that those who follow Him will become like Him (Matt. 10:25). What does it mean to **"be like Jesus"** in today's complex world? Matthew paints eight portraits of what Christlikeness looks like, including admitting our vulnerability to temptation.*

#4: To Be Like Jesus Means TO ADMIT OUR VULNERABILITY TO TEMPTATION

Matthew's inclusion of the temptation is remarkable. It shows that the sinless Lord of the universe was tempted, just as we are (Heb. 4:15–16). If we want to be like Jesus, we must accept that temptation is real—as is the possibility of overcoming temptation. But we need to be open about our struggles. In doing so we honor God, recognize the power of sin, and encourage others to do likewise.

1. Most of us continually battle against at least one temptation. What tempts you? How can you overcome this temptation?

2. Jesus was tired, thirsty, and hungry when the devil tempted Him. What does this indicate to you about Satan's willingness to take advantage of you while you are down?

3a. Jesus was not alone in the desert. Who was with Him?

_____

_____

3b. How are these same companions working in your life?

_____

_____

_____

4. How did Jesus use Scripture as His primary weapon against Satan (vv. 4, 7, 10)?

_____

_____

5. How did the devil attempt to use Scripture against Jesus (v. 6)?

_____

_____

_____

——◆ Dealing with Temptations ◆——

God promises to help you overcome temptation, but He also expects you to do your part. When you find yourself in a tempting situation, it's not enough to say, "Well, Lord, if You didn't want me to be doing this, You would have gotten me out of this mess!" Notice that Scripture says God will provide "the way of escape" (1 Cor. 10:13), but it is up to you to take the appropriate action to escape the temptation.

 1 Corinthians 10:1–13

[1]Moreover, brethren, I do not want you to be unaware that all our fathers were under the cloud, all passed through the sea, [2]all were baptized into Moses in the cloud and in the sea, [3]all ate the same spiritual food, [4]and all drank the same spiritual drink. For they drank of that spiritual Rock that followed them, and that Rock was Christ.

continued

continued

⁵But with most of them God was not well pleased, for *their bodies* were scattered in the wilderness.

⁶Now these things became our examples, to the intent that we should not lust after evil things as they also lusted. ⁷And do not become idolaters as *were* some of them. As it is written, "The people sat down to eat and drink, and rose up to play." ⁸Nor let us commit sexual immorality, as some of them did, and in one day twenty-three thousand fell; ⁹nor let us tempt Christ, as some of them also tempted, and were destroyed by serpents; ¹⁰nor complain, as some of them also complained, and were destroyed by the destroyer. ¹¹Now all these things happened to them as examples, and they were written for our admonition, upon whom the ends of the ages have come.

¹²Therefore let him who thinks he stands take heed lest he fall. ¹³No temptation has overtaken you except such as is common to man; but God *is* faithful, who will not allow you to be tempted beyond what you are able, but with the temptation will also make the way of escape, that you may be able to bear *it.*

PAY ATTENTION TO TEMPTATION!

Paul's warning to "take heed lest [you] fall" *(1 Cor. 10:12) is as necessary today as it has ever been. For we, like all who have gone before us, are fallen, temptable, and subject to thinking and doing what is wrong. Few teachings of Scripture have more practical implications for day-to-day living.*

Opportunities for temptation are almost endless. And since human nature is not getting any better, nor is any of us immune to the corrupted appetites of the flesh, we need to take Paul's warning seriously and watch out for temptation, or we will surely fall. Yet Scripture offers several alternatives for dealing with temptation as we find it:

(1) We should *avoid* temptation whenever possible. Proverbs 4:14–15 urges us, "Do not enter the path of the wicked, and do not walk in the way of evil. Avoid it, do not travel on it." Often we know beforehand whether a certain set of circumstances is likely to lead to sin. Therefore, the obvious way to avoid sin is to avoid those circumstances. Paul described a "way of escape" from temptation (1 Cor. 10:13). Often the escape is to stay away from the place or the people where temptation lurks.

As believers, we can help others in this regard. We can avoid setting up situations that encourage people to do wrong. Teachers, for example, can help students avoid cheating by making assignments, giving tests, and communicating expectations in ways that reduce the need or incentive to cheat. Likewise, business owners and managers can devise procedures that don't needlessly place employees in a position where they might be tempted to steal cash, inventory, or equipment. It's not that a teacher or employer can't trust

continued

continued
students or employees, but that no one can trust human nature to be immune from temptation.

(2) We should *flee* from powerful temptations. Earlier in this letter, Paul warned the Corinthians to flee sexual immorality (6:18). Here he warned them to flee idolatry (v. 14). Elsewhere he warned Timothy to flee the lust for material possessions and wealth (1 Tim. 6:9–11), as well as youthful lusts (2 Tim. 2:22). The message is clear: don't toy with temptation. Flee from it!

(3) Chronic temptation is something we need to *confess* and offer to Christ and ask for His cleansing work. Some temptations are powerful inner struggles, with thoughts and attitudes that graphically remind us of how fallen we really are. What should we do with that kind of temptation? Rather than deny it or try to repress it, we should bring it to Christ. He alone is capable of cleaning up the insides of our minds.

(4) Finally, we must *resist* temptation until it leaves us.

When Christ was tempted by the devil, He resisted until the devil went away (Matt. 4:1–11). James encouraged us to do the same (James 4:7). Resistance begins by bathing our minds with the Word of God and standing our ground. We have the promise, after all, that the temptations we experience will never go beyond the common experiences of others, or beyond our ability to deal with them (1 Cor. 10:13). That is great news! ◆

---

1. When you encounter trials, tribulations, or temptations, how do you usually respond? Check all that apply.

    _____ Why me, Lord?
    _____ What did I do to deserve this?
    _____ God, what do You want me to learn from this?
    _____ I can handle this.

2. Why is attempting to escape temptation not a cowardly action?

    _____

    _____

    _____

3. In 1 Corinthians 10:13, the apostle Paul lists five encouraging truths about temptation. List these five points in your own words.

    _____

    _____

    _____

    _____

    _____

4. How does the fact that God will not allow you to be tempted beyond what you can bear comfort you?

_____

_____

_____

——◆ Hey, Nobody's Perfect! ◆——

In 1986, Les Kolakowski, a Polish philosopher, said, "I remember seeing on American television a young man who was convicted of brutally raping a child, a little girl; his comment was, 'Everybody makes mistakes.' And so, we now know who raped the child; 'everybody,' that is, nobody."

The philosopher's poignant comment was prophetic. Our society has become a convocation of victims. It is okay to shoot someone if you were abused as a child. If the earth quakes or the floodwaters rise, it is all right for you to rob a store since the store's insurance company will cover the loss. After all, it isn't your fault these things happen. You are the victim.

Besides, the enticement to sin is strong. Satan offers an entire array of pleasures, all of which imply, "There's a whole lot more to life than just going to church, reading your Bible, and living that 'dull' Christian life." Satan makes it sound so easy to obtain life's pleasures.

But these are just excuses. The bottom line is that we give in to temptation because we are weak. God will help us, though. All we have to do is submit our lives to Him.

THE ROOTS OF SIN

Excuses for sin are many: "The devil made me do it"; "I couldn't help myself"; "It's not really my fault"; "I'm only human."

James mentions another excuse that people give for sin: they blame God (James 1:13). "If only He understood how hard it is to overcome temptation," they say. "He put me in a situation that was more than I could handle."

But the problem with that way of thinking is that sin is never rooted outside of us; it always comes from our own heart, often from our desire for what God has not given us (1:14–15).

In this sense, the roots of sin lie in covetousness or discontentment. We feel that we are worthy of more than what we have. But that means that sin is tied closely to pride—and God resists the proud (James 4:6).

But He gives grace to the humble. Therefore, the surest path to overcoming the temptation is to develop humility, which leads to contentment with the good gifts of God (James 1:17–18).

 James 1:2–18

²My brethren, count it all joy when you fall into various trials, ³knowing that the testing of your faith produces patience. ⁴But let patience have *its* perfect work, that you may be perfect and complete, lacking nothing. ⁵If any of you lacks

continued

continued

wisdom, let him ask of God, who gives to all liberally and without reproach, and it will be given to him. ⁶But let him ask in faith, with no doubting, for he who doubts is like a wave of the sea driven and tossed by the wind. ⁷For let not that man suppose that he will receive anything from the Lord; ⁸*he is* a double-minded man, unstable in all his ways.

⁹Let the lowly brother glory in his exaltation, ¹⁰but the rich in his humiliation, because as a flower of the field he will pass away. ¹¹For no sooner has the sun risen with a burning heat than it withers the grass; its flower falls, and its beautiful appearance perishes. So the rich man also will fade away in his pursuits.

¹²Blessed *is* the man who endures temptation; for when he has been approved, he will receive the crown of life which the Lord has promised to those who love Him. ¹³Let no one say when he is tempted, "I am tempted by God"; for God cannot be tempted by evil, nor does He Himself tempt anyone. ¹⁴But each one is tempted when he is drawn away by his own desires and enticed. ¹⁵Then, when desire has conceived, it gives birth to sin; and sin, when it is full-grown, brings forth death.

¹⁶Do not be deceived, my beloved brethren. ¹⁷Every good gift and every perfect gift is from above, and comes down from the Father of lights, with whom there is no variation or shadow of turning. ¹⁸Of His own will He brought us forth by the word of truth, that we might be a kind of firstfruits of His creatures.

"ALL WILL BE YOURS"

Satan promised to give Jesus authority over all the kingdoms of the world. "The father of lies" spoke the truth when he boldly declared, "This has been delivered to me, and I give it to whomever I wish" (Luke 4:6). He neglected, of course, to mention *who* had delivered the world powers to him—God the Son Himself, who possessed authority over the entire created universe (Col. 1:15–17)!

No wonder Jesus turned him down, one might say. But notice: Jesus did not respond by laying claim to His rightful authority. No, rather than focusing on the substance of the offer, He responded to its cost. To accept it would have required idolatry—a violation of His Father's unique position as the Lord God who *alone* deserves worship.

Jesus' response compels us to ask: When we receive an enticing offer that, in effect, promises "all will be yours" (4:7), what do we focus on—the benefits or the costs? The benefits may be extremely attractive. But what are the costs? Does it involve "selling out" our Lord by compromising His commands, His values, or His honor? If so, then the cost is simply too high, and we need to respond as He did: "Get behind me, Satan!"

 Luke 4:1–8

¹Then Jesus, being filled with the Holy Spirit, returned from the Jordan and was led by the Spirit into the wilderness, ²being tempted for forty days by the devil. And in those days He ate nothing, and afterward, when they had ended, He was hungry.

³And the devil said to Him, "If You are the Son of God, command this stone to become bread."

⁴But Jesus answered him, saying, "It is written, 'Man shall not live by bread alone, but by every word of God.'"

continued

> *continued*
> ⁵Then the devil, taking Him up on a high mountain, showed Him all the kingdoms of the world in a moment of time. ⁶And the devil said to Him, "All this authority I will give You, and their glory; for *this* has been delivered to me, and I give it to whomever I wish. ⁷Therefore, if You will worship before me, all will be Yours."
> ⁸And Jesus answered and said to him, "Get behind Me, Satan! For it is written, 'You shall worship the LORD your God, and Him only you shall serve.'"

1. We rarely see sin in black and white. Temptation usually distorts our vision so sin appears in various shades of gray. Jesus, however, was quick to recognize the true cost of giving in to the devil. Identify the potential benefits and costs of following "gray" sins.
   a. "Borrowing" supplies from your employer

   Benefit: _____

   _____

   Cost: _____

   _____

   b. Filing questionable deductions on your taxes

   Benefit: _____

   _____

   Cost: _____

   _____

   c. Telling "white lies" to your spouse or children

   Benefit: _____

   _____

   Cost: _____

   _____

2. In Luke 4:5–8, Satan offered Jesus the world, if Christ would worship him. What has the devil offered you in hopes of distracting you from Jesus?

   _____

   _____

3. Satan often tempts us by telling us, "You've been so good lately. God wouldn't blame you if you took a little time off. Have some fun!" Why can't you afford to take a little time off?

_____

_____

_____

——◆ His Strength in Your Weakness ◆——

It was well past midnight when Dave's telephone rang. "Hello?" Dave mumbled into the receiver. "Who's this?"

"Dave, it's me—George," an insistent voice replied.

"Huh? Oh, George, What are you doing calling me in the middle of the night?"

"You're my friend, right? And you always said, 'Call if you need me.' Well, tonight I need you. Patti and I had a big fight. One thing led to another and I finally told her, 'I'm leaving and I'm never coming back!' She said, 'Fine, get going, and don't bother coming back.'

"I jumped in the car and started driving south. I'm calling you from a phone booth at some rest area. Dave, I'm tired and confused, and I don't know if I can take any more.

I'm tempted to keep driving until I come to a bar and go drown my sorrows. I'm thinking that if things don't look any better tomorrow, I'm going to buy a gun and be done with everything!"

"George, George! Calm down," Dave shouted into the telephone, reaching for his car keys. "Where are you exactly? Stay right there. I'm coming."

Two hours later, Dave found George at the rest area where his distraught friend had been waiting. They left together and found a restaurant, where they drank coffee and talked through George's troubles until daybreak. They prayed together and George poured his heart out to God.

They left George's car in the restaurant's parking lot and drove back home together.

George turned to Dave before getting out of the car. "Thanks, buddy," he said sincerely. "I don't know what I would have done if you hadn't answered the phone."

"I'm glad I was able to help you, George," Dave answered, "but don't forget that Jesus is always there for you, too."

"I'll keep that in mind!" George answered as he got out of the car and waved goodbye.

◆ ◆ ◆ ◆ ◆ ◆ ◆ ◆

None of us is strong all the time. Sometimes we are tempted to give in or give up, but right at our weakest moment, if we call out to Jesus, He will give us the strength to overcome temptation. If we neglect to call on Him, the results can be disastrous. ◆

PRAYERLESSNESS COMES BEFORE A FALL

Temptation is tough. It's a test. It's an enticement to do wrong. It may involve great pleasure, a chance to escape risk, or illegitimate gain. Whatever the offering, it's usually attractive.

But Scripture calls giving in to tempting opportunities sin. It even warns us that repeatedly giving way to temptation can result in falling away permanently with a total loss

continued

continued

of interest in returning to God (Heb. 6:6–8, according to one interpretation). Clearly we need God's strength, and wisdom to flee (1 Cor. 6:18; 1 Tim. 6:11).

As Jesus and His closest companions faced great danger, they were afraid and tired (Luke 22:42–45). Jesus knew how vulnerable and confused that condition can make a person. He urged His followers to join Him in prayer so that they would not fall into temptation (Luke 22:40). They could not face the trials to come without new strength from God.

Earlier Jesus had taught His followers to ask the Father not to lead them into temptation (Matt. 6:13). There is no sin in being tempted. In fact, temptation is a sign that our spiritual lives are strong enough to recognize values that conflict with godliness. But giving in is sin. That's why it's crucial to take time to declare to God our weakness, weariness, and need for help in the midst of testing.

It may also help to have others pray with us, just as Jesus did in His hour of need. Do you have others you can turn to for prayer in times of difficulty? Are you available when others have that need?

 Luke 22:39–46

³⁹Coming out, He went to the Mount of Olives, as He was accustomed, and His disciples also followed Him. ⁴⁰When He came to the place, He said to them, "Pray that you may not enter into temptation."

⁴¹And He was withdrawn from them about a stone's throw, and He knelt down and prayed, ⁴²saying, "Father, if it is Your will, take this cup away from Me; nevertheless not My will, but Yours, be done." ⁴³Then an angel appeared to Him from heaven, strengthening Him. ⁴⁴And being in agony, He prayed more earnestly. Then His sweat became like great drops of blood falling down to the ground.

⁴⁵When He rose up from prayer, and had come to His disciples, He found them sleeping from sorrow. ⁴⁶Then He said to them, "Why do you sleep? Rise and pray, lest you enter into temptation."

1. Think of a time when you felt as if your world were caving in around you. In what ways were you vulnerable and confused?

_____

_____

2. How would you rate your communication with God during times of temptation? Circle one.

Awful	Fair	Satisfactory	Good	Wonderful
1	2	3	4	5

3. In Luke 22:39–46, Jesus warned His disciples twice to pray so they would not enter into temptation. What specific temptations do you think Jesus had in mind?

_____

_____

4. What is the cup Jesus refers to in Luke 22:42?

_____

_____

5. After Jesus successfully resisted temptation in the garden, an angel came to minister to Him. His wilderness experience and this occasion are the only references in the New Testament where angels ministered to Jesus during His earthly life. Why did the angels help Jesus?

_____

_____

_____

◆ Strength in Weakness ◆

Think about a time when you felt like your life was collapsing before you, and there was nothing you could do to stop it. How did you get through this time?

One of the great paradoxes in the Christian life is that when you are at your weakest, your faith in Jesus causes you to be your strongest. How can this be?

WHEN I AM WEAK, THEN I AM STRONG

Our world prizes strength—the physical strength of athletes, the financial strength of companies, the political strength of officeholders, and the military strength of armies. But Paul put a new twist on the notion of strength: weakness can make a person strong (2 Cor. 12:7–10).

Most of us would have no problem with God using our natural areas of strength, such as speaking, organizing, managing, or selling. But suppose He chose instead to use us in areas where we are weak? Moses claimed to be a poor speaker (Ex. 4:10), yet God used him as His spokesman on Israel's behalf. Peter tended to be impulsive and even hotheaded, yet God used him as one of the chief architects of the early church.

Weakness has a way of making us rely on God far more than our strengths do. What weakness in your life might God desire to use for His purposes?

2 Corinthians 12:7–10

[7]And lest I should be exalted above measure by the abundance of the revelations, a thorn in the flesh was given to me, a messenger of Satan to buffet me, lest I be exalted above measure. [8]Concerning this thing I pleaded with the Lord three times that it might depart from me. [9]And He said to me, "My grace is sufficient for you, for My strength is

continued

continued
made perfect in weakness." Therefore most gladly I will rather boast in my infirmities, that the power of Christ may rest upon me. ¹⁰Therefore I take pleasure in infirmities, in reproaches, in needs, in persecutions, in distresses, for Christ's sake. For when I am weak, then I am strong.

In 2 Corinthians 12:7, Paul mentions that he was plagued by a "thorn in the flesh." Bible scholars have debated for years about the nature of this thorn. Some scholars interpret it to be a physical infirmity that Paul wanted removed. Others view it as an emotional problem. And some scholars believe Paul's thorn was a spiritual defect in one of the fledgling congregations he had pioneered.

Ironically, Paul never said what the thorn was that bothered him. He did describe it, however, as a "messenger of Satan," and he asked God three times to remove it.

God didn't, though. Instead, He told Paul, "My grace is sufficient for you" (2 Cor. 12:9). In other words, God was telling His apostle, "Paul, I am all you need."

♦ ♦ ♦ ♦ ♦ ♦ ♦ ♦ ♦

1. What "thorn in the flesh" have you recently experienced?

_____

_____

_____

2. How was this situation resolved? Did you recognize God's hand in this resolution?

_____

_____

_____

3. How was God's strength "made perfect in weakness" (12:9) in Paul's life?

_____

_____

_____

4. How has God been able to use your weaknesses to strengthen you?

_____

_____

_____

——— ◆ Forgiven Again? ◆ ———

For most believers, there are certain sins that continually tempt us. We know certain behavior is wrong, but something inside leads us to commit the same sin many times. We ask God to forgive us, but we may wonder if He will continue to forgive us for committing the same sin.

Don't get discouraged. God will not turn His back on us. If we sincerely ask God to set us straight, He will do just that. Be careful, though, about asking for forgiveness when you know in your heart that you are not willing to turn away from the tempting situation. An insincere request for forgiveness does no good.

God is concerned with our attitudes. He wants us to be willing to let Jesus help us turn away from sin. If we are willing, Christ will work in us to give us the strength we need to overcome temptation.

FORGIVENESS ABOUNDS

Do you ever feel hopeless regarding your faith? Do you doubt God's willingness to forgive you over and over again?

Peter (John 21:15) might easily have felt that way. He had risen to a position of leadership among Jesus' followers. He had even been given the "keys of the kingdom" (Matt. 16:19). And he had positioned himself as the defender of Christ when Roman soldiers came to arrest Him (John 18:10). But when he felt the heat of a national trial, conviction, and death, Peter denied three times that he even knew Christ (John 18:15–18, 25–27) and afterward disappeared. What Jesus had predicted about him came true (John 13:31–38).

So when Jesus engaged Peter in a conversation on the shore (John 21:15–23), Peter might easily have felt that he was already disqualified from further service for the Lord. After all, as we would say, three strikes and you're out. But Jesus reconnected with Peter and called him to genuine love and the continuation of His work.

Second and third chances are not often available in families, communities, or workplaces. All you have to do is fail once too often, and you're gone. But Christ offers tangible love and boundless forgiveness—to those who own up to their failures and repent (Luke 7:47). Can we offer anything less to our coworkers, families, and friends?

 John 21:15–23

¹⁵So when they had eaten breakfast, Jesus said to Simon Peter, "Simon, *son* of Jonah, do you love Me more than these?"

He said to Him, "Yes, Lord; You know that I love You."

He said to him, "Feed My lambs."

¹⁶He said to him again a second time, "Simon, *son* of Jonah, do you love Me?"

He said to Him, "Yes, Lord; You know that I love You."

He said to him, "Tend My sheep."

¹⁷He said to him the third time, "Simon, *son of* Jonah, do you love Me?" Peter was grieved because He said to him the third time, "Do you love Me?"

And he said to Him, "Lord, You know all things; You know that I love You."

Jesus said to him, "Feed My sheep. ¹⁸Most assuredly, I say to you, when you were younger, you girded yourself and walked where you wished; but when you are old, you will stretch

continued

> *continued*
> out your hands, and another will gird you and carry *you* where you do not wish." ¹⁹This He spoke, signifying by what death he would glorify God. And when He had spoken this, He said to him, "Follow Me."
> ²⁰Then Peter, turning around, saw the disciple whom Jesus loved following, who also had leaned on His breast at the supper, and said, "Lord, who is the one who betrays You?" ²¹Peter, seeing him, said to Jesus, "But Lord, what *about* this man?"
> ²²Jesus said to him, "If I will that he remain till I come, what *is that* to you? You follow Me."
> ²³Then this saying went out among the brethren that this disciple would not die. Yet Jesus did not say to him that he would not die, but, "If I will that he remain till I come, what is *that* to you?"

1. Why do you think Jesus questioned Peter's love for him three times (John 21:15–23)?

_____

_____

_____

2. How did Peter know that Jesus had truly forgiven him?

_____

_____

_____

3. How can you extend Christ's forgiveness to your family, friends, and coworkers?

_____

_____

_____

4. What is Jesus saying to Peter when He tells him to tend and feed His sheep (John 21:15–17)?

_____

_____

_____

_____

Temptation touches all of us. Although we want to do the right thing, we are curiously drawn toward evil. If we allow Jesus to help us through tempting situations, He will keep us from sinning.

That's not to say that we will never sin again. As we strive to be more like Jesus, we are constantly growing. From time to time, we succumb to Satan's attempt to tempt and tantalize us. When we have relapses, we need to repent and allow Christ to keep us on track.

The key questions now are, "How can we continue the process? How can we stay on the path with Christ and keep moving in the right direction?" In our next chapter, we will discover some answers to these questions and some "secrets" of spiritual staying power!

CHAPTER 8

KEEPING THE BIG PICTURE

Pete was excited—spring was in the air! The neighbors were busy cleaning out their garages, weeding and fertilizing their lawns, and adding fresh flowers and mulch to their landscaping.

Although Pete normally considered mowing the grass to be mundane, he was now looking forward to working in his yard. He had already serviced his lawn mower, sprayed off the dirt from the exterior, and filled the tank with gasoline. He could hardly wait to get started!

Pete pulled the engine crank and the mower roared to life. He methodically pushed the mower across the lawn, leaving behind a bright green path and the sweet fragrance of freshly mowed grass. Suddenly, the sound of metal grating against metal pierced the air above the din of the motor.

He quickly realized that the awful noise was coming from his mower's engine. Suddenly, the lawn mower became silent and motionless.

"Oh, no! What's wrong with my mower?" Pete cried. He attempted to restart the engine, but the mower wouldn't budge. Finally, Pete resigned himself to taking the mower to a service center.

The repairman checked a few levers, tinkered with the gas line, and tugged at the mower's starter. He grimaced when he opened the oil cap. "There's no oil in the crankcase!" he said to Pete. "When was the last time you put oil in this thing?"

Pete's heart sank. "Oh, I can't believe I did that! I drained all the old oil out of the mower, but I forgot to refill it. No wonder the engine blew up!"

◆ ◆ ◆ ◆ ◆ ◆ ◆ ◆ ◆

Something similar happens in our lives when we ask God for forgiveness, allowing Him to clean out our lives, but fail to follow God, allowing Him to fill our lives with His presence. Our lives were not intended to be spiritual vacuums. If our hearts are not filled with Christ's love, we become attractive targets for Satan.

Getting rid of the sin in your life is a great place to start your spiritual journey, but it is a lousy place to stop. The only safe and secure life is one that is continually filled with the love and power of Jesus Christ.

TURNING BACK IS AWFUL

Do you intend to overcome evil? If so, make sure to replace it with good or else, as Jesus warns, the evil may return with its friends, producing more evil than ever (Matt. 12:43–45).

This teaching warns us to persevere in the journey of faith. That can be hard to do when everything in us wants to quit, the way an exhausted long-distance runner wants to drop out of a marathon. Besides (we reason), look how far we've already come!

Yes, but God's goal is not just to make us nicer people

continued

continued
or better people, but to make us Christlike *people*.
That won't happen completely until we're with
Him. For now, He wants us to keep growing in
that direction. Stopping short can bring disaster.
In a warning similar to Jesus' words here, the
writer of Hebrews urges us to "go on to perfec-
tion" and describes in sobering words the fate of
those who "fall away" (Heb. 6:1–12).
    Fortunately, God lends us help to prevent us
from falling back. As Hebrews also says, He disci-
plines us for our good. His stern efforts can feel
harsh, but they are the loving protection of a car-
ing Father (Matt. 12:3–11). ◆

 Matthew 12:43–45

⁴³"When an unclean spirit goes out of a man, he goes through dry places, seeking rest, and finds none. ⁴⁴Then he says, 'I will return to my house from which I came.' And when he comes, he finds *it* empty, swept, and put in order. ⁴⁵Then he goes and takes with him seven other spirits more wicked than himself, and they enter and dwell there; and the last *state* of that man is worse than the first. So shall it also be with this wicked generation."

1. Which of the following activities have you tried, but after a while your interest began to wane? Check all that apply.

_____ Going on a diet
_____ Saving money
_____ Reading the entire Bible in one year
_____ Exercising regularly
_____ Attending church or Bible studies

2. How does trusting in Jesus differ from trying a new experience?

_____

_____

3. In Matthew 12:43–45, Jesus uses a graphic illustration to teach a lesson about the Jews' rejection of the true Messiah and their subsequent openness to satanic deception. With this story in mind, describe some of the dangers of starting to follow Christ, but not continuing.

_____

_____

_____

_____

4. What are some potential temptations that Satan may use to try to get you to disclaim your faith in Christ?

_____

_____

_____

_____

5. What steps can you take to keep growing in your spiritual life, preventing spiritual "back-sliding"?

_____

_____

_____

◆ Counting the Cost ◆

You have probably heard someone say, "I'd give anything if I could learn to play the piano," or, "I'd give anything if I could get my college degree." Often these people are being less than honest in making such statements. Why? Because learning to play the piano or getting a college degree are real possibilities for most everyone in this country.

The question is usually not, "Can I achieve these goals?" The more accurate question is, "Am I willing to pay the price in time, money, effort, and sacrifice to accomplish the goal?"

One of two reasons explains why most people would not really "give anything" to obtain a goal: Either the goal itself does not merit such sacrifice, or a person is unwilling to make the sacrifice.

When it comes to the kingdom of God, Jesus encouraged people to count the costs. It's as if He says, "Go ahead, check Me out. See if following Me is worth the price. Look as closely as you want; you won't be disappointed."

THE INCOMPARABLE VALUE OF THE KINGDOM

The two parables in Matthew 13:44–46 describe the incomparable value of the kingdom. Nothing was worth more, Jesus told His followers. Nothing is too great to sacrifice for it—certainly not material wealth (Matt. 6:33; 19:16–30).

In light of Jesus' words here, maybe it's worth pausing to reflect on your own life and choices. What has your commitment to Christ cost you? Or has it cost you anything? Has it made any difference in decisions about your career, lifestyle, investments, or purchases? What would you sell in order to gain the King and His kingdom (v. 46)?

Matthew 13:44–46

⁴⁴"Again, the kingdom of heaven is like treasure hidden in a field, which a man found and hid; and for joy over it he goes and sells all that he has and buys that field.

⁴⁵"Again, the kingdom of heaven is like a merchant seeking beautiful pearls, ⁴⁶who, when he had found one pearl of great price, went and sold all that he had and bought it."

1a. What is the largest single purchase you have ever made? (For instance, a business, a house, a boat.)

_____

_____

1b. What did you have to sacrifice to make that purchase?

_____

_____

2. In Matthew 13:44–46, Jesus compares the kingdom of heaven to a field and to a pearl. What are the similarities between these two stories?

_____

_____

_____

3. What is the main difference between the two stories in regard to the relationship of the discoverer to the discovery?

_____

_____

4. Why is the price of following Jesus worth the investment?

_____

_____

_____

◆ Renewing Your Spiritual Energy ◆

Most of us are familiar with rechargeable tools. When they are fully charged, you take it for granted that they will help you perform whatever task they are designed to do. But, just as you are in the middle of finishing an important chore, it happens. The tool's power begins to fade, and then it dies.

Now what can you do? Not much, at least not with that tool. You must wait until your helpful tool's battery is recharged before you can continue using it.

In some ways, our spiritual lives are similar to rechargeable tools. While we are fully charged, we operate smoothly and efficiently. But to keep from losing our charge, we need to be renewed, and this need for restoration is constant.

Why? Because much of life tends to drain our spiritual energy. Thankfully, we can turn to Jesus for the energy boost we need. Gathering with a community of believers for worship and fellowship also helps to recharge our "spiritual batteries."

BEING RENEWED AND RENEWED

A person of faith among non-believing coworkers can face misunderstanding, challenges to his or her values, or outright opposition. One's lifestyles, convictions, and even "workstyle" can trigger such responses. It can be very draining, like swimming against the tide.

The new believers in Acts felt stress, too. They encountered the arrest of their leaders (4:1–3), rage and plots against them (4:25), and threats (4:21, 29). In response, they prayed together and were filled with the Holy Spirit yet again (4:31). The previous filling (2:4) needed to be renewed.

As modern-day believers we, too, face the drain of unfriendly encounters in our lives and work. Like the Christians in Acts, we need to gather regularly for spiritual refueling. Worship services and small groups can provide that essential element, supplying the power we need to follow Christ in this world.

Do you have such a place? If not, consider gathering a small group of believers at your job or in your neighborhood to pray together and talk about life in Christ.

 Acts 4:31

³¹And when they had prayed, the place where they were assembled together was shaken; and they were all filled with the Holy Spirit, and they spoke the word of God with boldness.

1. What are the "Top Three Spiritual Energy Drainers" you are dealing with in your life right now?

_____

_____

_____

_____

2. What "spiritual rechargers" did you discover in Acts 4:31?

_____

_____

3. How can you tap into the power available through these rechargers?

_____

_____

——◆ Finishing the Race ◆——

Andrew had always dreamed of participating in a marathon. He trained every day after work, hoping that some day he could make the dream come true.

Finally, Andrew had the opportunity to register for a local marathon. The morning of the event, he was so excited he could barely wait for the race to begin. He had been working so hard for so long—Andrew was about to live his dream!

The runners took their places and the marathon began. Andrew had just established a steady pace when catastrophe struck. Another runner had come up behind Andrew and accidentally tripped him.

Before Andrew realized what happened, he was sprawled out on the pavement, his ankle throbbing and beginning to swell. He managed to get to the side of the road, and the realization that he had sprained his ankle sunk in.

The paramedics arrived and treated the injured ankle. They were about to carry Andrew back to the first aid tent, but he refused to go. "I have dreamed of running in a marathon for too long. I'm finally here—I am going to finish the race."

And that is exactly what Andrew did. His fellow runners had finished the race hours before Andrew did, but as far as he was concerned, he had won the race.

◆ ◆ ◆ ◆ ◆ ◆ ◆ ◆ ◆

Many Christians start the race of life well. They run wholeheartedly for a while, but then fatigue, frustration, and sometimes sheer exhaustion deplete their spiritual passion.

God is concerned that you not only start the Christian life well, but He also wants you to finish the race! How can you prevent such devastating results in your life? ◆

FINISHING WELL

What would be an appropriate epitaph on your tombstone? What statement would describe your life overall rather than whatever current circumstances you are temporarily facing right now?

When Paul wrote to the believers in Thessalonica, they were in the midst of intense suffering (2 Thess. 1:4–5). But Paul encouraged them to look beyond their immediate troubles to the return of Christ and the affirmation they would receive from Him at that time (vv. 6–7). Their enemies, who were really enemies of the Lord, would be judged and dealt with (vv. 8–9). By contrast, they would

continued

continued

join with their Savior in joy and praise (v. 10). Paul went on in the next chapter to expand on this theme and its impact on the Thessalonians' current difficulties (2:1–12).

God calls us as His people to finish our lives well by holding on to the truths that last (2:15). He challenges us to maintain

lifelong faithfulness and not to be entirely caught up in the here and now, whether good or bad.

As you consider the long-term direction of your life, what memories are you creating in others about your values and reputation? What will people choose to remember about you?

---

2 Thessalonians 1:3–12

³We are bound to thank God always for you, brethren, as it is fitting, because your faith grows exceedingly, and the love of every one of you all abounds toward each other, ⁴so that we ourselves boast of you among the churches of God for your patience and faith in all your persecutions and tribulations that you endure, ⁵*which is* manifest evidence of the righteous judgment of God, that you may be counted worthy of the kingdom of God, for which you also suffer; ⁶since *it is* a righteous thing with God to repay with tribulation those who trouble you, ⁷and to *give* you who are troubled rest with us when the Lord Jesus is revealed from heaven with His mighty angels, ⁸in flaming fire taking vengeance on those who do not

know God, and on those who do not obey the gospel of our Lord Jesus Christ. ⁹These shall be punished with everlasting destruction from the presence of the Lord and from the glory of His power, ¹⁰when He comes, in that Day, to be glorified in His saints and to be admired among all those who believe, because our testimony among you was believed.

¹¹Therefore we also pray always for you that our God would count you worthy of *this* calling, and fulfill all the good pleasure of *His* goodness and the work of faith with power, ¹²that the name of our Lord Jesus Christ may be glorified in you, and you in Him, according to the grace of our God and the Lord Jesus Christ.

---

1. Describe a situation in your past when you were tempted to quit but didn't. What kept you from quitting?

_____

_____

_____

2. At times, the Thessalonian believers probably felt like quitting, too—especially since they were continually confronted with intense persecutions because of their faith. What motivation does Paul point out that might encourage these Christians (and us, too!) to continue following Christ to the end?

_____

_____

_____

3. What keys do you find in 2 Thessalonians 1:4 that are crucial to surviving in the midst of trials and tribulations?

_____

_____

_____

_____

4. How does keeping your focus on the future rewards and judgment of God affect your conduct in the present?

_____

_____

_____

——◆ Expand Your Vision! ◆——

Leigh had a problem. She had just been told by the doctor that her mother would never be able to walk normally again. Leigh's forty-eight-year-old mother had contracted a new disease known as post polio syndrome. Now they had to break the news to her mother.

Leigh went into the examining room with the doctor, where Jane was anxiously waiting for her test results. "Mom, we have some news for you," Leigh began.

The doctor stepped in to explain the disease and the impending results. "Jane, you may be able to walk with a cane in six months—maybe a year. But eventually you will need a wheelchair to help you get around."

Jane's normally cheerful, vibrant voice was noticeably shaken as she asked the doctor, "Are you saying that there's no cure for this disease?"

"Not yet; we're still trying to understand exactly how the disease affects people."

Jane thought for a moment, and then she looked into her daughter's eyes. "Well, I suppose this is happening for a reason. All I can do is make the best of it. Doctor, what can I do to help you learn more about this disease?"

◆ ◆ ◆ ◆ ◆ ◆ ◆ ◆ ◆

To Jane, her disease was but a momentary discomfort and inconvenience to be overcome. Jane went on to allow many specialists to run numerous tests on her to learn more about the disease. She also tried different pain-management techniques to find an effective form of relief

As Jane learned more about her condition, she formed a post polio syndrome support group in her community. Now, she is organizing various projects to raise money for research.

Like Jane, we also need to avoid getting bogged down by the tyranny of a present, temporary crisis. We need to keep our vision focused on the big picture. ◆

KEEPING THE BIG PICTURE

Where were you ten years ago? Does it seem like a distant memory, or as if it were only yesterday? Does the here and now totally consume you, dominating your perspective? Where do you expect to be ten years from now?

As Peter neared the end of his life, he wrote a letter in which he offers some insight into the nature of time and eternity. He beckons us to view time in both thousand-year units and as mere days (2 Peter 3:8), recalling the beginnings of creation (vv. 4–6). He also projects into the future, when judgment will be rendered and new heavens and earth will be home to those who fear God (vv. 10–13). Peter reminds us that God values a day as much as a thousand years, affirming the importance of the here and now (v. 8). But he also affirms God's activity long before we came on the scene (v. 9).

Peter's perspective challenges us to live with a view toward eternity and values that last—purity, holiness, and righteousness (vv. 11, 14). We need to avoid getting caught up in the here and now and losing sight of our eternal destiny. Neither the joys of today nor the problems of this week can quite compare with what God has prepared for us in eternity. Peter urges us to stick with the basics of the faith and resist the fleeting enticements offered in this present moment (vv. 17–18).

 2 Peter 3:8–18

[8]But, beloved, do not forget this one thing, that with the Lord one day *is* as a thousand years, and a thousand years as one day. [9]The Lord is not slack concerning *His* promise, as some count slackness, but is longsuffering toward us, not willing that any should perish but that all should come to repentance.

[10]But the day of the Lord will come as a thief in the night, in which the heavens will pass away with a great noise, and the elements will melt with fervent heat; both the earth and the works that are in it will be burned up. [11]Therefore, since all these things will be dissolved, what manner *of persons* ought you to be in holy conduct and godliness, [12]looking for and hastening the coming of the day of God, because of which the heavens will be dissolved, being on fire, and the elements will melt with fervent heat? [13]Nevertheless we, according to His promise, look for new heavens and a new earth in which righteousness dwells.

[14]Therefore, beloved, looking forward to these things, be diligent to be found by Him in peace, without spot and blameless; [15]and consider *that* the longsuffering of our Lord *is* salvation—as also our beloved brother Paul, according to the wisdom given to him, has written to you, [16]as also in all his epistles, speaking in them of these things, in which are some things hard to understand, which untaught and unstable *people* twist to their own destruction, as *they do* also the rest of the Scriptures.

[17]You therefore, beloved, since you know *this* beforehand, beware lest you also fall from your own steadfastness, being led away with the error of the wicked; [18]but grow in the grace and knowledge of our Lord and Savior Jesus Christ.

To Him *be* the glory both now and forever. Amen.

1. Time races by so quickly it seems. What decisions or events have had the most profound impact on your life so far? (For instance, getting married or the death of a parent.)

2. Most of us are extremely time conscious. We read time-management books, watch the clock, and carry organizers to keep our schedules straight. Few people are truly eternity conscious. How does your concept of time management compare with that of God's? (See 2 Peter 3:8.)

_____

_____

_____

3. How would you answer someone who claims that God's Word is irrelevant and that the prophecies concerning His rewards and judgment will never really come to pass?

_____

_____

_____

◆ ◆ ◆ ◆ ◆ ◆ ◆ ◆ ◆

Sometimes it is easy to become discouraged as a Christian, especially when things are not going your way or you are persecuted for your faith. But knowing Jesus and living for Him is worth any price we must pay.

The New Testament believers seemed to pulsate with the power of the Holy Spirit, despite difficult circumstances. Persecution and pressure served only to intensify their spiritual passion.

They lived with an awareness that Jesus could return at any moment, and that motivated them to take risks, overcome obstacles, and speak bravely about Christ to others. In the next chapter, we will explore ways we can witness to our generation with that same sort of power, and hopefully with the same impact!

SHOW AND TELL

Once there was an extraordinarily successful fisherman. Each morning he took his small boat out on the lake, and within a few hours, he returned with a huge catch of fish. Anyone who witnessed his unusual success at fishing wondered how he could catch so many fish.

One day a stranger showed up at the docks and asked the man if he could go along the next time the infamous fisherman went fishing.

"Sure," said the master fisherman. "Meet me here at five o'clock tomorrow morning."

Early the next morning, the two men made their way through the dawn mist to a small cove. The fisherman stopped the boat and cut the engine. The master fisherman began preparing his pans and pails as though he were expecting a large catch of fish.

Meanwhile, the stranger watched in amused bewilderment because the fisherman didn't even have a fishing rod. He didn't have any exotic lures, nor did he have any tempting bait. All he had was a small net and an old tackle box.

Slowly, the fisherman pulled the tackle box over to him, carefully opened it, and reached inside. When he removed his hand from the box,

he was holding a ten-inch stick of dynamite! Without a word of explanation, the fisherman took out a match and lit the fuse. He held the sizzling stick in his hand and watched it burn down dangerously close to the end before he finally tossed the dynamite into the water.

An enormous blast beneath the surface of the lake reverberated through the morning stillness. Almost immediately the startled and stunned fish started coming to the surface of the lake. The fisherman systematically dipped his net in the water and started filling up his pans and pails with fish.

The stranger cried out, "Ah-hah! So that's how you do it, huh? That's how you catch so many fish. Well, you can't fish like that in these waters." With that, he reached into his hip pocket, pulled out his wallet, and whipped out his game warden's badge. "You are under arrest!" he said sternly. "Now quit netting those fish."

The fisherman didn't even

blink an eye. He simply reached into his tackle box, pulled out another stick of dynamite, lit it, held onto it for a few moments, then handed the dynamite to the game warden. In a slow, confident drawl the fisherman said, "Now, are you going to just sit there, or are you going to fish?"

◆ ◆ ◆ ◆ ◆ ◆ ◆ ◆ ◆

Although this story is fictitious, it reminds us that God asks us a similar question: Are you just going to sit there, or are you going to fish?

Jesus has called us to be fishers of men, and He has filled us with the power of His Holy Spirit so we can be His witnesses. Yet many Christians are reluctant to tell others about Jesus. They may fear being rejected or making a mistake. Some believers hope that people will simply notice the difference Christ has made in their lives. But Jesus has called us to proclaim His message to others in addition to living a Christian lifestyle.

WHAT IT MEANS TO BE LIKE JESUS

*Jesus indicated that those who follow Him will become like Him (Matt. 10:25). What does it mean to **"be like Jesus"** in today's complex world? Matthew paints eight portraits of what Christlikeness looks like, including:*

#5: To Be Like Jesus Means TO PROCLAIM THE MESSAGE OF CHRIST

Jesus' life was *not* an open book, readable by all. To be sure, He lived a perfect, model life. But even that could not stand alone as an undeniable witness. His actions needed interpretation. So He supplemented His good *deeds* with good *news*. In the same way, we need to verbally declare our faith if we want to be like Christ. Certainly we need to back up our words with a Christlike lifestyle. But what we tell others gives meaning to our quiet walk and good deeds.

THE GOOD NEWS

WHILE WE WERE STILL SINNERS CHRIST DIED FOR US . . . .

 Matthew 4:12–25

12Now when Jesus heard that John had been put in prison, He departed to Galilee. 13And leaving Nazareth, He came and dwelt in Capernaum, which is by the sea, in the regions of Zebulun and Naphtali, 14that it might be fulfilled which was spoken by Isaiah the prophet, saying:

15 "The land of Zebulun and the land of Naphtali,
  By the way of the sea, beyond the Jordan, Galilee of the Gentiles:
16 The people who sat in darkness have seen a great light,
  And upon those who sat in the region and shadow of death
  Light has dawned."

17From that time Jesus began to preach and to say, "Repent, for the kingdom of heaven is at hand."

18And Jesus, walking by the Sea of Galilee, saw two brothers, Simon called Peter, and Andrew his brother, casting a net into the sea; for they were fishermen. 19Then He said to them, "Follow Me, and I will make you fishers of men." 20They immediately left *their* nets and followed Him.

21Going on from there, He saw two other brothers, James *the son* of Zebedee, and John his brother, in the boat with Zebedee their father, mending their nets. He called them, 22and immediately they left the boat and their father, and followed Him.

23And Jesus went about all Galilee, teaching in their synagogues, preaching the gospel of the kingdom, and healing all kinds of sickness and all kinds of disease among the people. 24Then His fame went throughout all Syria; and they brought to Him all sick people who were afflicted with various diseases and torments, and those who were demon-possessed, epileptics, and paralytics; and He healed them. 25Great multitudes followed Him—from Galilee, and *from* Decapolis, Jerusalem, Judea, and beyond the Jordan.

1. Jesus calls us to be "fishers of men" (Matt. 4:19). Compare proclaiming Christ's message to the following statements about fishing:

I must go where the fish are and move on when they are not biting.

_____

_____

I need various bait, hooks, and tackle for different kinds of fish.

_____

_____

I can bait the hook any way I want, but I can't make the fish bite.

_____

_____

2. The willingness of Peter, Andrew, James, and John to immediately walk away from their work to follow Jesus is amazing. What does the prompt obedience of these men suggest to you about Jesus' call for you to follow Him?

_____

_____

_____

3. List several ways you can become a fisherman for Christ.

_____

_____

_____

◆ Knowledge Is Power ◆

A witness is someone who has personal knowledge of a person or an event. If you genuinely know Jesus, you are automatically qualified to be a witness for Him. The better you know Jesus and the more you learn about how His Word works in your life, the more information you have to present when you are sharing the Good News with someone else.

Jesus lived out the gospel, but He also told people about God. If Jesus had only done works of compassion, His mission would have been incomplete. If Jesus had only listened to the heartbreak and despair of people's lives and given them encouraging words, He still would not have fulfilled God's plan. But because Jesus proclaimed God's saving Word and modeled it, we can understand the true meaning of the gospel and its implications for our lives.

You don't need to be a Bible scholar to tell others about the love, joy, and peace that can be found through Christ. You can simply share from your own experience. "Jesus changed my life for the better!" is a valid testimony, and one that is hard to contest if your lifestyle is consistent with your words.

SOME BASICS OF WITNESS

What exactly does it mean to "witness"? Many people associate the term with street evangelism. But street preachers can sometimes alienate people, although the boldness of their faith is acknowledged by all. What else, then, is needed for someone to be an effective representative for Christ?

John was one of Jesus' closest associates. In this first chapter of his first letter, John notes several basic elements of what it means to communicate Christ to others:

- Our message grows out of our knowledge and experience of Christ (1 John 1:1–4).

- We make clear to others what we have heard from Christ (v. 5).
- We live out our faith on a continuous basis, thereby avoiding lives that contradict our message (vv. 6–7). "Walk" is a metaphor for living used often in the New Testament (for example, John 8:12; Rom. 4:12; Col. 3:7).
- When we fall short (as we all will, v. 10), we own up to it, avoiding deception about our walk or Christ's work (vv. 8–10).

Truthfulness, clarity, consistency, and honesty should be basic qualities of Christ's followers. They are things that last in the eyes of God, and they matter most to those evaluating the faith. We should offer nothing less.

---

 1 John 1:1–10

¹That which was from the beginning, which we have heard, which we have seen with our eyes, which we have looked upon, and our hands have handled, concerning the Word of life— ²the life was manifested, and we have seen, and bear witness, and declare to you that eternal life which was with the Father and was manifested to us— ³that which we have seen and heard we declare to you, that you also may have fellowship with us; and truly our fellowship is with the Father and with His Son Jesus Christ. ⁴And these things we write to you that your joy may be full.

⁵This is the message which we have heard from Him and declare to you, that God is light and in Him is no darkness at all. ⁶If we say that we have fellowship with Him, and walk in darkness, we lie and do not practice the truth. ⁷But if we walk in the light as He is in the light, we have fellowship with one another, and the blood of Jesus Christ His Son cleanses us from all sin.

⁸If we say that we have no sin, we deceive ourselves, and the truth is not in us. ⁹If we confess our sins, He is faithful and just to forgive us *our* sins and to cleanse us from all unrighteousness. ¹⁰If we say that we have not sinned, we make Him a liar, and His word is not in us.

1. What makes you decide whether or not you will believe someone's account of an event?

_____ My best friend told me about it.
_____ I saw it on the evening news.
_____ The government said it happened that way.
_____ The person who told me about it was an eyewitness.

2. List some of the reasons why John's witness in 1 John 1:1–3 is credible and should be believed.

_____

_____

_____

_____

3. What do you think John meant when he said, "God is light" (1 John 1:5)?

_____

_____

_____

_____

4. What are some ways a Christian might "walk in darkness" and as a result, destroy his or her fellowship with God (vv. 5–6)?

_____

_____

_____

_____

5. Why is it important that we admit when we sin (vv. 8–10)?

_____

_____

_____

_____

◆ Integrity Counts! ◆

Bonnie was the new secretary for the music department of a big church, and it was her first day on the job. As one of her first responsibilities, Bonnie's boss asked her to make fifty photocopies of a piece of sheet music for choir practice that night.

But when Bonnie looked at the sheet music, she saw a copyright notice at the bottom of the page which clearly prohibited the duplication of the music without written permission from the publisher. Bonnie showed the notice to her boss. After all, the church preached against stealing, didn't it? Surely she wouldn't be asked to violate the law.

When Bonnie's boss saw the notice, he laughed and said, "Oh, don't worry about that, Bonnie. We aren't copying the music to sell it. Oh, when you're done with that, would you mind copying that new computer program on my desk. Joe bought the software and is letting us use it; he says it will really help us keep track of our music."

◆ ◆ ◆ ◆ ◆ ◆ ◆ ◆ ◆

The foundation of a believer's witness must be honesty and integrity. If we are not honest in how we present Christ to others, they will see right through us. And if our lifestyles are not consistent with the biblical values we claim to believe, the nonbeliever has every right to question the validity of our beliefs. ◆

A STRAIGHTFORWARD APPROACH

Many people in today's culture have grown cynical about religion. So as we believers think about presenting the gospel to others, we need to be careful to make our message credible and straightforward.

Paul mentions two dangers that he avoided so as not to compromise his credibility (1 Thess. 2:5): the use of "flattering words," which amounts to telling people what they want to hear, and "a cloak for covetousness," which involves hidden motives. To use either of these approaches is to deceive people. That's unacceptable for someone who presents himself as a representative of Christ.

The key to Paul's integrity was his realization that God Himself had entrusted him with the message (2:4). The task of taking the gospel to the Gentiles was not something that Paul had thought up, but a calling from God (Gal. 1:11–17). Thus his aim was not to please people, but God.

Nor did he need to worry about his material well-being, even less to covet what others had. As a messenger of God, he could rely on God to provide for his needs and remain content in whatever circumstances came his way (Phil. 4:11–12).

As we consider ways in which to communicate Christ to people around us, what obstacles to our credibility might there be? Are there things about our methods or motives that conflict with the message with which we've been entrusted?

---

 1 Thessalonians 2:4–12

⁴But as we have been approved by God to be entrusted with the gospel, even so we speak, not as pleasing men, but God who tests our hearts. ⁵For neither at any time did we use flattering words, as you know, nor a cloak for covetousness—God is witness. ⁶Nor did we seek glory from men, either from you or from others, when we

continued

continued
might have made demands as apostles of Christ. 7But we were gentle among you, just as a nursing *mother* cherishes her own children. 8So, affectionately longing for you, we were well pleased to impart to you not only the gospel of God, but also our own lives, because you had become dear to us. 9For you remember, brethren, our labor and toil; for laboring night and day, that we might not be a burden to any of you, we preached to you the gospel of God.

10You *are* witnesses, and God *also,* how devoutly and justly and blamelessly we behaved ourselves among you who believe; 11as you know how we exhorted, and comforted, and charged every one of you, as a father *does* his own children, 12that you would walk worthy of God who calls you into His own kingdom and glory.

1. When someone is trying to sell you something, and that person smothers you with flattery, how does that make you feel about the product?

_____ I'll buy whatever that person is selling.

_____ I assume the product must be inferior if the salesperson must resort to such methods.

_____ I'm suspicious of the salesperson, but I consider the product on its own merits.

2. Why couldn't the Thessalonians accuse the apostle Paul of having ulterior motives in presenting the gospel to them (1 Thess. 2:4–12)?

_____

_____

_____

3. What was there about Paul's relationship with God that prevented him from using deceitful methods when presenting the gospel?

_____

_____

_____

——◆ Are You on Your Own? ◆——

The idea of being a witness for Christ can be overwhelming. It's a big responsibility to feel like it is entirely up to you to convince nonbelievers to follow Jesus. Fortunately, though, this responsibility is not yours alone. It is the Holy Spirit who actually speaks to a person's heart. From there, it is God who actually convinces a person to believe.

You cannot save anyone by yourself. Consider this: if you, by your persuasive powers alone, can talk somebody into becoming a Christian, then someone more persuasive than you can possibly talk them out of being a Christian!

But, when the Holy Spirit convinces a person of the need for Christ and that person truly trusts and accepts Christ, an eternal commitment takes place that nobody can discredit.

Your job is to be a vessel through which God can present His message. God only requires that you be faithful and obedient to His Word. The success or failure of your witness is ultimately in God's hands.

CARROTS, NOT STICKS

As believers, we are called to proclaim the message of Christ to unbelievers in the best way we know how, being faithful to the truth. That's really all that Peter did at Pentecost (Acts 2:14–36), but his speech produced dramatic results: the small band of Christ's followers added 3,000 believers that day (v. 41).

In the same way, each of us needs to speak up as best we can when the opportunity presents itself. What we say will reflect our understanding of the faith at the time. We may not sound as impressive as Peter or a minister or some other believer. But at least our message will be authentic.

Notice that Peter did not call for an immediate response. Only after God's Spirit had "cut to the heart" those in the audience and they asked for help (v. 37) did he explain what they ought to do (v. 38).

In the same way we need to offer the "carrot" of truth to others—the facts of the gospel and our experience of it—and let the Holy Spirit wield the "stick" of conviction. We should strive for impact and understanding before pressing for a decision. That might take weeks or years, or just moments. But we need the sensitive timing of a midwife as we assist in the spiritual birthing process.

Acts 2:37–41

37Now when they heard *this*, they were cut to the heart, and said to Peter and the rest of the apostles, "Men *and* brethren, what shall we do?"

38Then Peter said to them, "Repent, and let every one of you be baptized in the name of Jesus Christ for the remission of sins; and you shall receive the gift of the Holy Spirit. 39For the promise is to you and to your children, and to all who are afar off, as many as the Lord our God will call."

40And with many other words he testified and exhorted them, saying, "Be saved from this perverse generation." 41Then those who gladly received his word were baptized; and that day about three thousand souls were added *to them*.

---

1. How does knowing that it is God who does the converting of nonbelievers liberate you in your witnessing?

2. Offering "carrots" when we witness does not mean we ignore the tough questions concerning God, Jesus, or the Bible. It does mean that we should attempt to keep our witnessing as positive as possible. Think of someone you may want to share the gospel with. What are some "carrots" you might be able to offer that person?

_____

_____

_____

3. What are some of the key elements of conversion to Christ?

_____

_____

_____

◆ ◆ ◆ ◆ ◆ ◆ ◆ ◆ ◆

The gospel is the Good News about Jesus Christ, and evangelism is sharing that message with the world. But for evangelism to be effective, a knowledgeable, willing messenger—not a technique or a program—must carry the Good News to those who need to hear it.

Have you ever wondered why God doesn't simply have a news conference on international television and deliver His message to the world? Wouldn't that be a more efficient use of time and energy? Why would He be willing to entrust something as vital as the gospel to us?

Scripture doesn't exactly say, but the Bible does indicate that each generation of believers is responsible to reach the unbelievers of that generation with the gospel. Maybe the best witnesses are those who know what it means to have been lost, but now are found—sinners who realized they were on their way to destruction, but when they called out to Jesus, He saved them.

The apostle Peter may have had that in mind when he told people who finally recognized their sinfulness that they needed to repent. The word repent *means to change your mind, your heart, and your attitudes, but it also means to change your direction in life.*

Most of us are reluctant to change; we resist change whenever possible. In the next chapter, we will discover that some changes in life can be exciting and extremely positive.

NEW WINE, NEW WINESKINS

Someone has defined a rut as being "a grave with the ends knocked out of it," and this definition is probably not far from the truth. When your life gets in a rut, you are more reluctant to change; the only alternative to change is stagnancy, which slowly sucks the life out of you.

When you think about the boredom and tedium you stand to face, however, you will realize that you can't afford not to change! Change can bring exciting opportunities; it can also be painful and even frightening at times.

You may be excited about beginning a new career. There will be new things to learn and challenges to spark your creativity. But what happens if you hate the job? What if it doesn't meet your expectations? What if you fail?

Who needs all that stretching and growing? Why not leave well enough alone? Wouldn't life be much easier if you could snuggle down on your comfortable couch, pull a blanket around your shoulders, and live life vicariously through your favorite television programs?

Maybe. But it's not possible to do that because Jesus wants you to change and grow. And, while most of us say we are in favor of change, when it comes down to actually making a change, we are resistant. We like doing things the old way.

The old way is familiar and comfortable, like an old friend. Most of us do not want to tamper with something that is just fine like it is.

Another factor in our acceptance or rejection of change is whether or not we are the ones suggesting the change. We usually support the changes we have initiated. It's those changes that are imposed on us that cause the problems—those things over which we have little or no control. And, more often than not, we are not the ones to initiate change.

Nevertheless, you can't avoid change. Whether you want to or not, you are going to experience some major changes in life. But that's fine. We have Someone to help us through times of change.

WHAT IT MEANS TO BE LIKE JESUS

Jesus indicated that those who follow Him will become like Him (Matt. 10:25). What does it mean to **"be like Jesus"** *in today's complex world? Matthew paints eight portraits of what Christlikeness looks like, including:*

#6: To Be Like Jesus Means TO COMMIT TO CHANGED THINKING AND BEHAVIOR

In His Sermon on the Mount, Jesus explained the values of the kingdom. Money, prayer, relationships, possessions, information, and power were a few of the categories He redefined from God's perspective. He showed that following Him will involve radical change for most of us. It may mean undoing the way we've always done things and rethinking traditional sources of wisdom from our parents and culture. To become like Jesus involves a tough-minded review of our values and a thorough change in our behavior.

THE SERMON ON THE MOUNT

Repent, for the kingdom of heaven is at hand," Jesus warned as He began His public ministry in Galilee (Matt. 4:17). His message quickly spread and huge crowds came to hear Him from Galilee, from nearby Syria and the Decapolis, and from as far away as Jerusalem, Judea, and east of the Jordan River (4:24–25).

They came to hear about a kingdom. Instead, Jesus talked about a lifestyle—the lifestyle of those who intend to live in the kingdom. As perhaps thousands gathered on a hillside (or "mountain," 5:1; the exact location is unknown), Jesus began to fill out the implications of His appeal for repentance. It would mean far more than an outward show of piety. Indeed, Jesus urged His listeners to make such a complete change of heart and life that they would "be perfect, just as your Father in heaven is perfect" (5:48).

Jesus may have spoken the contents of Matthew 5–7, known as the Sermon on the Mount, on more than one occasion. It is possible that the address lasted for some time as He described the new lifestyle of the kingdom, holding it up like a jewel with many facets, to be examined from many different angles. On the other hand, bits and pieces of the sermon can be found throughout the gospels. Like any good teacher, Jesus probably repeated much of His teaching at other times and places in order to drive home the message.

The Sermon on the Mount contains the core of Jesus' moral and ethical teaching:

The Beatitudes (5:3–12). True happiness comes from looking at life from God's perspective, which is often the reverse of the human point of view.

Salt and Light (5:13–16). Jesus wants His followers to influence the moral and spiritual climate of the world.

The Morality of the Kingdom (5:17–48). Jesus' listeners were familiar with the Old Testament Law and with the many traditions that generations of rabbis had added to it. But Jesus revealed a morality that went beyond the letter of the Law to its spirit.

Spiritual Disciplines (6:1–18). Practicing religion certainly involves behavior, but it goes beyond an outward show of spirituality to the hidden quality of one's character.

Treasures on Earth (6:19–34). Our relationship to money and material possessions reveals much about our relationship to God. Jesus does not denounce worldly goods, but He urges His listeners to place ultimate value on the treasures of heaven.

Judging Right and Wrong (7:1–6). Most of us are quick to point out the moral flaws of others. Jesus warns us to pay more attention to our own.

Asking and Receiving (7:7–12). When we approach God with a request, we can expect Him to deal with us as a loving father deals with his child. And just as God deals with us in love, He expects us to deal with others in love.

A Challenge to Obedience (7:13–29). Jesus wraps up His message with a challenge to change. The alternatives are clear: living a lifestyle that is worthy of the kingdom, resulting in life and joy; or ignoring the way of Christ, resulting in death and disaster.

In this manner, Jesus described the lifestyle of the kingdom. When He was finished, Matthew says that the people were "astonished" at His teaching (7:28; literally "overwhelmed" or "stunned"). They had come to hear a new teacher, but this one exceeded their expectations. His voice had an unusual but unmistakable ring of authority (7:29). And no wonder: they were listening to the King Himself! ◆

Matthew 5:1—7:27

[1]And seeing the multitudes, He went up on a mountain, and when He was seated His disciples came to Him. [2]Then He opened His mouth and taught them, saying:

3   "Blessed *are* the poor in spirit,
        For theirs is the kingdom of heaven.
4   Blessed *are* those who mourn,
        For they shall be comforted.
5   Blessed *are* the meek,
        For they shall inherit the earth.
6   Blessed *are* those who hunger and thirst
            for righteousness,
        For they shall be filled.
7   Blessed *are* the merciful,
        For they shall obtain mercy.
8   Blessed *are* the pure in heart,
        For they shall see God.
9   Blessed *are* the peacemakers,
        For they shall be called sons of
            God.
10   Blessed are those who are persecuted for
            righteousness' sake,
        For theirs is the kingdom of heaven.

[11]"Blessed are you when they revile and persecute you, and say all kinds of evil against you falsely for My sake. [12]Rejoice and be exceedingly glad, for great *is* your reward in heaven, for so they persecuted the prophets who were before you.

[13]"You are the salt of the earth; but if the salt loses its flavor, how shall it be seasoned? It is then good for nothing but to be thrown out and trampled underfoot by men.

[14]"You are the light of the world. A city that is set on a hill cannot be hidden. [15]Nor do they light a lamp and put it under a basket, but on a lampstand, and it gives light to all *who are* in the house. [16]Let your light so shine before men, that they may see your good works and glorify your Father in heaven.

[17]"Do not think that I came to destroy the Law or the Prophets. I did not come to destroy but to fulfill. [18]For assuredly, I say to you, till heaven and earth pass away, one jot or one tittle will by no means pass from the law till all is fulfilled. [19]Whoever therefore breaks one of the least of these commandments, and teaches men so, shall be called least in the kingdom of heaven; but whoever does and teaches *them,* he shall be called great in the kingdom of heaven. [20]For I say to you, that unless your righteousness exceeds *the righteousness* of the scribes and Pharisees, you will by no means enter the kingdom of heaven.

[21]"You have heard that it was said to those of old, 'You shall not murder, and whoever murders will be in danger of the judgment.' [22]But I say to you that whoever is angry with his brother without a cause shall be in danger of the judgment. And whoever says to his brother, 'Raca!' shall be in danger of the council. But whoever says, 'You fool!' shall be in danger of hell fire. [23]Therefore if you bring your gift to the altar, and there remember that your brother has something against you, [24]leave your gift there before the altar, and go your way. First be reconciled to your brother, and then come and offer your gift. [25]Agree with your adversary quickly, while you are on the way with him, lest your adversary deliver you to the judge, the judge hand you over to the officer, and you be thrown into prison. [26]Assuredly, I say to you, you will by no means get out of there till you have paid the last penny.

[27]"You have heard that it was said to those of old, 'You shall not commit adultery.' [28]But I say to you that whoever looks at a woman to lust for her has already committed adultery with her in his heart. [29]If your right eye causes you to sin, pluck it out and cast *it* from you; for it is more profitable for you that one of your members perish, than for your whole body to be cast into hell. [30]And if your right hand causes you to sin, cut it off and cast *it* from you; for it is more profitable for you that one of your members perish, than for your whole body to be cast into hell.

continued

continued

31"Furthermore it has been said, 'Whoever divorces his wife, let him give her a certificate of divorce.' 32But I say to you that whoever divorces his wife for any reason except sexual immorality causes her to commit adultery; and whoever marries a woman who is divorced commits adultery.

33"Again you have heard that it was said to those of old, 'You shall not swear falsely, but shall perform your oaths to the Lord.' 34But I say to you, do not swear at all: neither by heaven, for it is God's throne; 35nor by the earth, for it is His footstool; nor by Jerusalem, for it is the city of the great King. 36Nor shall you swear by your head, because you cannot make one hair white or black. 37But let your 'Yes' be 'Yes,' and your 'No,' 'No.' For whatever is more than these is from the evil one.

38"You have heard that it was said, 'An eye for an eye and a tooth for a tooth.' 39But I tell you not to resist an evil person. But whoever slaps you on your right cheek, turn the other to him also. 40If anyone wants to sue you and take away your tunic, let him have *your* cloak also. 41And whoever compels you to go one mile, go with him two. 42Give to him who asks you, and from him who wants to borrow from you do not turn away.

43"You have heard that it was said, 'You shall love your neighbor and hate your enemy.' 44But I say to you, love your enemies, bless those who curse you, do good to those who hate you, and pray for those who spitefully use you and persecute you, 45that you may be sons of your Father in heaven; for He makes His sun rise on the evil and on the good, and sends rain on the just and on the unjust. 46For if you love those who love you, what reward have you? Do not even the tax collectors do the same? 47And if you greet your brethren only, what do you do more *than others?* Do not even the tax collectors do so? 48Therefore you shall be perfect, just as your Father in heaven is perfect.

CHAPTER 6

1"Take heed that you do not do your charitable deeds before men, to be seen by them. Otherwise you have no reward from your Father in heaven. 2Therefore, when you do a charitable deed, do not sound a trumpet before you as the hypocrites do in the synagogues and in the streets, that they may have glory from men. Assuredly, I say to you, they have their reward. 3But when you do a charitable deed, do not let your left hand know what your right hand is doing, 4that your charitable deed may be in secret; and your Father who sees in secret will Himself reward you openly.

5"And when you pray, you shall not be like the hypocrites. For they love to pray standing in the synagogues and on the corners of the streets, that they may be seen by men. Assuredly, I say to you, they have their reward. 6But you, when you pray, go into your room, and when you have shut your door, pray to your Father who *is in the secret place;* and your Father who sees in secret will reward you openly. 7And when you pray, do not use vain repetitions as the heathen *do.* For they think that they will be heard for their many words.

8"Therefore do not be like them. For your Father knows the things you have need of before you ask Him. 9In this manner, therefore, pray:

> Our Father in heaven,
> Hallowed be Your name.
> 10   Your kingdom come.
> Your will be done
> On earth as *it is* in heaven.
> 11   Give us this day our daily bread.
> 12   And forgive us our debts,
> As we forgive our debtors.
> 13   And do not lead us into temptation,
> But deliver us from the evil one.
> For Yours is the kingdom and the power
> and the glory forever. Amen.

14"For if you forgive men their trespasses, your heavenly Father will also forgive you. 15But if you do not forgive men their trespasses, neither will your Father forgive your trespasses.

16"Moreover, when you fast, do not be like the hypocrites, with a sad countenance. For they disfigure their faces that they may appear to men

continued

continued

to be fasting. Assuredly, I say to you, they have their reward. 17But you, when you fast, anoint your head and wash your face, 18so that you do not appear to men to be fasting, but to your Father who *is* in the secret *place;* and your Father who sees in secret will reward you openly.

19"Do not lay up for yourselves treasures on earth, where moth and rust destroy and where thieves break in and steal; 20but lay up for yourselves treasures in heaven, where neither moth nor rust destroys and where thieves do not break in and steal. 21For where your treasure is, there your heart will be also.

22"The lamp of the body is the eye. If therefore your eye is good, your whole body will be full of light. 23But if your eye is bad, your whole body will be full of darkness. If therefore the light that is in you is darkness, how great *is* that darkness!

24"No one can serve two masters; for either he will hate the one and love the other, or else he will be loyal to the one and despise the other. You cannot serve God and mammon.

25"Therefore I say to you, do not worry about your life, what you will eat or what you will drink; nor about your body, what you will put on. Is not life more than food and the body more than clothing? 26Look at the birds of the air, for they neither sow nor reap nor gather into barns; yet your heavenly Father feeds them. Are you not of more value than they? 27Which of you by worrying can add one cubit to his stature?

28"So why do you worry about clothing? Consider the lilies of the field, how they grow: they neither toil nor spin; 29and yet I say to you that even Solomon in all his glory was not arrayed like one of these. 30Now if God so clothes the grass of the field, which today is, and tomorrow is thrown into the oven, *will He* not much more *clothe* you, O you of little faith?

31"Therefore do not worry, saying, 'What shall we eat?' or 'What shall we drink?' or 'What shall we wear?' 32For after all these things the Gentiles seek. For your heavenly Father knows that you need all these things. 33But seek first the kingdom of God and His righteousness, and all these things shall be added to you. 34Therefore do not worry about tomorrow, for tomorrow will worry about its own things. Sufficient for the day *is* its own trouble.

CHAPTER 7

1"Judge not, that you be not judged. 2For with what judgment you judge, you will be judged; and with the measure you use, it will be measured back to you. 3And why do you look at the speck in your brother's eye, but do not consider the plank in your own eye? 4Or how can you say to your brother, 'Let me remove the speck from your eye'; and look, a plank *is* in your own eye? 5Hypocrite! First remove the plank from your own eye, and then you will see clearly to remove the speck from your brother's eye.

6"Do not give what is holy to the dogs; nor cast your pearls before swine, lest they trample them under their feet, and turn and tear you in pieces.

7"Ask, and it will be given to you; seek, and you will find; knock, and it will be opened to you. 8For everyone who asks receives, and he who seeks finds, and to him who knocks it will be opened. 9Or what man is there among you who, if his son asks for bread, will give him a stone? 10Or if he asks for a fish, will he give him a serpent? 11If you then, being evil, know how to give good gifts to your children, how much more will your Father who is in heaven give good things to those who ask Him! 12Therefore, whatever you want men to do to you, do also to them, for this is the Law and the Prophets.

13"Enter by the narrow gate; for wide *is* the gate and broad *is* the way that leads to destruction, and there are many who go in by it. 14Because narrow *is* the gate and difficult *is* the way which leads to life, and there are few who find it.

15"Beware of false prophets, who come to you in sheep's clothing, but inwardly they are ravenous wolves. 16You will know them by their fruits.

continued

continued

Do men gather grapes from thornbushes or figs from thistles? [17]Even so, every good tree bears good fruit, but a bad tree bears bad fruit. [18]A good tree cannot bear bad fruit, nor *can* a bad tree bear good fruit. [19]Every tree that does not bear good fruit is cut down and thrown into the fire. [20]Therefore by their fruits you will know them.

[21]"Not everyone who says to Me, 'Lord, Lord,' shall enter the kingdom of heaven, but he who does the will of My Father in heaven. [22]Many will say to Me in that day, 'Lord, Lord, have we not prophesied in Your name, cast out demons in Your name, and done many wonders in Your name?' [23]And then I will declare to them, 'I never knew you; depart from Me, you who practice lawlessness!'

[24]"Therefore whoever hears these sayings of Mine, and does them, I will liken him to a wise man who built his house on the rock: [25]and the rain descended, the floods came, and the winds blew and beat on that house; and it did not fall, for it was founded on the rock.

[26]"But everyone who hears these sayings of Mine, and does not do them, will be like a foolish man who built his house on the sand: [27]and the rain descended, the floods came, and the winds blew and beat on that house; and it fell. And great was its fall."

1. Rank the following experiences according to the amount of change they have brought to your life (1 = the most change; 6 = the least change).

    _____ Getting your driver's license
    _____ Getting married
    _____ Having a baby
    _____ Having a teenager
    _____ Moving to a new area
    _____ Starting a new job

2. Why do you think most of us are reluctant to change?

    _____

    _____

    _____

3. According to Matthew 7:21–27, what is the true test of Christ's transforming power in our lives?

    _____

    _____

    _____

    _____

4. What are three areas of your behavior that you will seek God's help in changing?

_____

_____

_____

_____

◆ Charting the Wrong Course ◆

The merchant's small boat crashed through another massive wave, drenching the man and everything in the tiny vessel. The night was dark and stormy—the kind of night that sailors describe when they are telling their stories, only this was the real thing.

The sea raged against the rugged man's efforts to keep the boat from capsizing. The rain, wrapped in a cold, whistling wind, pelted his face as he attempted to guide the little vessel up the Canadian North Atlantic coast. The merchant could not see where he was going, so he had no choice but to rely on his compass to guide him.

As the merchant battled through the murky waters, he began to worry that something was seriously wrong. "I should have been there by now," he said. Suddenly, to his horror and surprise, he realized the answer to his problem. He was not moving north as his compass had indicated; he was headed due east, straight into the open sea! Desperately, he wrestled against the furious wind and waves and was finally able to turn the small craft back to shore.

The next day, the merchant carefully examined his boat for damages and discovered the reason for his compass's inaccurate readings. He had recently taken the boat in for repairs, part of which required a new compass. Apparently, when the man who was installing the new compass was setting the screws that held it in place, he ran out of pure brass screws. Assuming that a slight compromise would be insignificant, he found a screw made of a ferrous alloy and finished the job with that.

Consequently, the magnetic tip of the compass was attracted to the alloyed metal and would not produce true readings. The merchant discovered—almost tragically too late—that while he thought he had been charting his course by the magnetic North Pole, the craft had actually been charting its own course. It was an accident waiting to happen.

◆ ◆ ◆ ◆ ◆ ◆ ◆ ◆ ◆

A similar situation exists in our lives before we trust Jesus. Most of us chart our own course, thinking that we are moving in the right direction and not realizing that our "inner compasses" are defective. Unless you have allowed Christ to guide you, your inner compass will continue giving you inaccurate, undependable readings.

One of the first steps you must take to follow Christ is to repent of your sins. You must allow Jesus to change not only your course, but also to change the center of your life. ◆

THE KING DECLARES HIS KINGDOM

Jesus initiated His public life with a simple but stiff challenge to repentance (Matt. 4:17). It was actually a familiar message—identical, in fact, to the message of John the Baptist, Jesus' forerunner (Matt. 3:2). Both urged their listeners to repent, *to change their minds and hearts, not merely for the sake of change, but in light of what they called "the kingdom."*

Jesus Is the King

The most important thing to notice is that a kingdom exists because Jesus is the King. He is the Messiah, the Savior promised by God in the Old Testament (Matt. 1:22–23; 2:6; Is. 7:14; Mic. 5:2). He is not only Israel's King, but the international Christ for all the nations. At the beginning of His life, magi came to Herod, asking where they could find the King of the Jews (Matt. 2:2). At the end of His life, Pilate asked Him, "Are you the King of the Jews?" He affirmed that He was (Matt. 27:11–12), and Pilate sanctioned His crucifixion on that basis (27:37).

So in Matthew 4:17–25, the King was declaring His kingdom. Foretold by Scripture and announced by John, Jesus had come to establish His rule. However, He disappointed the expectations of many people—both then and now.

Where Is the Kingdom?

For a few brief decades, Israel had enjoyed a relatively prosperous, peaceful monarchy under David and his son, Solomon. Some Old Testament passages prophesied that the Messiah would reestablish that sort of kingdom. Was now the time? Would Jesus overthrow the iron rule of the Romans and set up a political state? He did not. In fact, He told the Roman governor Pilate that His kingdom was not of this world, that He did not have an army fighting on His behalf (John 18:36). And He told the Pharisees that the kingdom was not something tangible and observable, but was "within" them (Luke 17:20).

Then is Christ's kingdom simply a spiritual concept, a powerful but abstract ideal? No, because He made a definite promise to His disciples that they would rule the tribes of Israel in His kingdom (Matt. 19:23, 28). They apparently took Him literally (Acts 1:6).

continued

continued

When Is the Kingdom?

No less puzzling is the question of when the kingdom has or will come. As they began their ministries, John the Baptist and Jesus declared that the kingdom was "at hand." But a few years later, when Jesus' followers asked whether He was ready to restore Israel's kingdom, He put them off; that was something that only His Father could know, He told them (Acts 1:6–7). Sometimes the kingdom seemed to be a present reality (Matt. 12:28; 13:18–23; 21:43). At other times, it seemed to be a hope for the future (Matt. 16:28; 20:20–23; 26:29).

Even today, theologians stridently debate over whether and in what form the kingdom has already been established, is currently in the process of being formed, is coming in the future, or is not coming at all. Like most questions that cannot be answered definitively to everyone's satisfaction, agreements are few and positions strongly defended.

What Is the Kingdom?

Is there any simple way to understand this puzzling doctrine of the kingdom? Probably not. Jesus' followers have not ceased to puzzle over His statements about it since the moment they were made. But most would generally agree that Christ's kingdom began in some way with His first coming. It continues to advance as His people live the gospel message throughout the world. However, it will not realize its ultimate completion until He returns.

What Difference Does It Make?

Whatever else we can say, the kingdom has to do with whatever Christ the King rules. That's why Jesus began His ministry with a call to repentance. Repentance means to change one's mind or purpose. In terms of the kingdom, it involves:

(1) A change in one's allegiance. If Christ is the King, He deserves our honor, loyalty, and obedience. We put ourselves under His authority and power. Whatever He says, we determine to do. That's the point of the oft-repeated lines in the Lord's Prayer, "Your kingdom come, Your will be done on earth as it is in heaven" (Matt. 6:10). Kingdom people submit their own will to the will of the King.

(2) A change in one's expectations. One of the difficulties people have with the idea of a kingdom is that it doesn't appear to be in place yet. The world seems to grow farther away from God by the day. As a result, it's easy to live for the here and now, as if this present life is all that matters. But the hope of the kingdom is that there is far more to life than what we see right now. Jesus made extraordinary promises in regard to a future kingdom, not only for Israel, but for all who follow Him as King.

(3) A change in one's values. Our culture values achievement, success, independence, and image. Other cultures value other qualities. But the values of the kingdom reflect what matters to the King. Jesus described a number of His values in Matthew 5:3–10, a section of the Sermon on the Mount known as the Beatitudes (or, as some call them, the "beautiful attitudes"). Kingdom people adopt the King's values and make choices that reflect those values.

(4) A change in one's priorities. The real test of people's values is how they spend their time and money. Jesus spoke directly to that issue in terms of the kingdom (Matt. 6:24–34). He did not demean the value of work or diminish the need for material goods. But He challenged His followers to bring kingdom values into their day-to-day lives. "Seeking first the kingdom" (Matt. 6:33) puts a Christlike perspective on one's work and its outcomes.

(5) A change in one's lifelong mission. Some people are driven to accomplish great tasks with their lives. Others live aimlessly from day to day, lacking purpose or direction. Either way, Jesus affects the outlook of a person's life. He gives His followers purpose and a mission—to live as subjects of the kingdom and promote kingdom values in everyday life and work. Ultimately, He wants His followers to extend His message to the ends of the earth. ◆

Matthew 4:17–25

17From that time Jesus began to preach and to say, "Repent, for the kingdom of heaven is at hand."

18And Jesus, walking by the Sea of Galilee, saw two brothers, Simon called Peter, and Andrew his brother, casting a net into the sea; for they were fishermen. 19Then He said to them, "Follow Me, and I will make you fishers of men." 20They immediately left *their* nets and followed Him.

21Going on from there, He saw two other brothers, James *the son* of Zebedee, and John his brother, in the boat with Zebedee their father, mending their nets. He called them, 22and imme-diately they left the boat and their father, and fol-lowed Him.

23And Jesus went about all Galilee, teaching in their synagogues, preaching the gospel of the kingdom, and healing all kinds of sickness and all kinds of disease among the people. 24Then His fame went throughout all Syria; and they brought to Him all sick people who were afflicted with var-ious diseases and torments, and those who were demon-possessed, epileptics, and paralytics; and He healed them. 25Great multitudes followed Him—from Galilee, and *from* Decapolis, Jerusa-lem, Judea, and beyond the Jordan.

1. If someone were to ask you to explain *repentance,* how would you do it?

_____

_____

_____

_____

2. Why do you think Jesus linked repentance with His announcement that the kingdom of heaven is at hand (Matt. 4:17)?

_____

_____

_____

_____

3. What changes have you allowed Jesus to help you make regarding your values, expecta-tions, and priorities?

_____

_____

_____

◆ Repentance Is More Than Being Sorry ◆

When you do something you're sorry for, do you simply say, "I'm sorry," or do you realize that the action itself was wrong and seek forgiveness because you have hurt God? Would you feel bad about certain actions if no one else knew you did them?

Unfortunately, many of us are not concerned so much about sinning itself; we are more concerned about getting caught! But what about the fact that our sins grieve God? We may worry about the discomfort in our lives that results from sin, but few of us dread sin simply because we know it is offensive to God.

Maybe that's why Jesus taught that in addition to renouncing sinful practices, we must also let go of improper ways of thinking about the changes He wants to make in our lives. Life with Christ is a whole new kind of living!

DOES CHANGE THREATEN YOU?

A stubborn allegiance to old habits and traditions can sometimes seriously hinder maturing faith. Every believer should pay attention to that, because new life in Christ inevitably leads to innovation and timely change. Fear of change is understandable, but too much fear may be a sign of sinful resistance or of clinging to the past only because it feels safe and familiar.

Jesus understood our human tendency toward predictability and the natural resistance to new things. He also knew that not all changes are good, and He never advocated change for the sake of change. But He warned against making tradition, particularly religious tradition, the standard by which all things should be tested (Luke 5:36–39). His parable of the wineskins pleads for at least the openness to consider something new. It affirms timely change in matters of growth and new life.

Are you resistant to the dynamics of change in your life, work, family, or church? If so, could you be resisting the very work of God or the ongoing dynamic of life itself? Pay attention to Jesus' image of the wineskins!

Luke 5:36–39

³⁶Then He spoke a parable to them: "No one puts a piece from a new garment on an old one; otherwise the new makes a tear, and also the piece that was *taken* out of the new does not match the old. ³⁷And no one puts new wine into old wineskins; or else the new wine will burst the wineskins and be spilled, and the wineskins will be ruined. ³⁸But new wine must be put into new wineskins, and both are preserved. ³⁹And no one, having drunk old *wine*, immediately desires new; for he says, 'The old is better.' "

1. How do you usually respond when you are faced with change?

_____ Go away. Leave me alone!
_____ Great, let's do it!
_____ That sounds fine for you, but count me out.
_____ I'm doing fine just the way I am, thank you.
_____ We've never done it that way before!
_____ Let me think about it.

2. In Jesus' parable about new wineskins, what does the new wine symbolize?

_____

_____

3. What is the difference between the changes Jesus encourages and "change for change's sake"?

_____

_____

_____

4. What "wineskins" need to be replaced in your life?

_____

_____

◆ An Eternal Chain Reaction ◆

Imagine that God were to give you a special mission where you were to travel across town to meet with your worst enemy. No doubt, you would probably be reluctant to complete the mission. But that's not the whole mission. God also informed you that you were to lay your hands on your enemy and pray for him! How do you think you might respond to such a request? With disbelief? Probably. With confusion and anger? Most likely.

Ananias probably experienced many of those same feelings when he received a vision from God to go and pray for Saul of Tarsus—Saul, whose notorious reputation for persecuting Christians preceded him. Nevertheless, Ananias overcame his misgivings and obeyed God.

A BIGOT DOES AN ABOUT-FACE

n Galatians 1:13–17, Paul recounts his dramatic confrontation with Christ on the Damascus road and his subsequent conversion (Acts 9:1–30). Imagine the emotional strain that was placed on Saul (as he was called at the time): Jesus was alive! What members of the Way (the early Christians) had been saying about Him was all true! And Saul had killed many of them! What a shattering experience for one "advanced in Judaism" and "exceedingly zealous for the traditions" of his fathers (Gal. 1:14).

continued

continued

Perhaps that's why God made Saul blind for three days. He had a lot to sort out after meeting the risen Lord. It's not easy for someone to suddenly revise the entire theological basis on which he's been living, especially as a respected leader. No one wants to admit he's been wrong. No wonder Saul spent much of the time in prayer.

But God not only intended to change Saul's theology; He was determined to transform his bigoted view of the world. At the root of Saul's intense hatred of the Christian movement might well have been a belief that it would destroy Judaism by mixing it with foreign, Gentile elements.

Imagine Saul's shock, then, when Ananias came to tell him that God had chosen him to bear His name—to the Gentiles (Acts 9:15; 22:14–15;

26:16–18)! Unthinkable! Jews like Saul, who were utterly committed to holy living by all the laws and traditions of Judaism, had nothing to do with Gentiles (Acts 10:28). No wonder it took Saul years to re-evaluate his perspectives and bring them in line with the heart of God for the world (Acts 9:26–30; 22:17–21).

Paul's experience forces us to ask: What attitudes of prejudice keep you from recognizing God's heart for the whole world? What attitudes of bigotry operate where you live or work? Do you in any way challenge that thinking, or do you just keep silent—or worse, go along with it or even promote it? Would God be able to use you to bear His name to people from a different ethnic heritage? ◆

 Galatians 1:13–17

[13]For you have heard of my former conduct in Judaism, how I persecuted the church of God beyond measure and *tried to* destroy it. [14]And I advanced in Judaism beyond many of my contemporaries in my own nation, being more exceedingly zealous for the traditions of my fathers.

[15]But when it pleased God, who separated me from my mother's womb and called *me* through His grace, [16]to reveal His Son in me, that I might preach Him among the Gentiles, I did not immediately confer with flesh and blood, [17]nor did I go up to Jerusalem to those *who were* apostles before me; but I went to Arabia, and returned again to Damascus.

Acts 9:10–19

[10]Now there was a certain disciple at Damascus named Ananias; and to him the Lord said in a vision, "Ananias."

And he said, "Here I am, Lord."

[11]So the Lord *said* to him, "Arise and go to the street called Straight, and inquire at the house of Judas for *one* called Saul of Tarsus, for behold, he is praying. [12]And in a vision he has seen a man named Ananias coming in and putting *his* hand on him, so that he might receive his sight."

[13]Then Ananias answered, "Lord, I have heard from many about this man, how much harm he has done to Your saints in Jerusalem. [14]And here he has authority from the chief priests to bind all who call on Your name."

[15]But the Lord said to him, "Go, for he is a chosen vessel of Mine to bear My name before Gentiles, kings, and the children of Israel. [16]For I will show him how many things he must suffer for My name's sake."

[17]And Ananias went his way and entered the house; and laying his hands on him he said, "Brother Saul, the Lord Jesus, who appeared to you on the road as you came, has sent me that you may receive your sight and be filled with the Holy Spirit." [18]Immediately there fell from his eyes *something* like scales, and he received his sight at once; and he arose and was baptized.

[19]So when he had received food, he was strengthened. Then Saul spent some days with the disciples at Damascus.

1. In Galatians 1:13–17, Paul shares part of his testimony of how his encounter with Jesus changed his life. What or whom has God used to get your attention and point your life in a different direction?

_____

_____

_____

_____

2. What impresses you most about Ananias's willingness to meet Saul (Acts 9:10–19)?

_____

_____

_____

3. When he finally stood face to face with Saul, Ananias greeted his former persecutor as "Brother." Why do you think he did this?

_____

_____

_____

4. Why would Saul's new mission have been a surprise to both him and Ananias?

_____

_____

_____

5. What attitudes of prejudice keep you from recognizing God's heart for the whole world? How can you alter this view?

_____

_____

_____

_____

Change is a part of life; each of us changes every day. And often we don't mind or notice slight changes. But, as soon as we are faced with major changes or those which we can't control, then change begins to bug us.

Trusting Jesus is a major change. He changes our priorities, our thinking, our aspirations, and our understanding of life itself. Jesus changes us from the inside out by changing our hearts and our attitudes, which in turn changes the way we function in the world. At times, some of the changes Jesus is bringing about in our lives may be disconcerting. But we can be certain of this: He always changes our lives for the better.

As you follow Christ, one of the areas of your life where you'll see change is in how you view service. Jesus talked quite a bit about being a servant—a servant to God and a servant to the entire world.

Most of us don't mind serving God. It's that part about serving others that raises doubt or resistance. In our next chapter, we'll discover the true meaning of being a servant.

THE SERVING SPIRIT

One of the many inspiring survival stories to come out of Fidel Castro's communist Cuba was Against All Hope *by Armando Valladares, a Christian whose only crime was speaking against communism. Valladares was thrown into Castro's prisons at the age of twenty-three and lived in horror and inhuman conditions for the next twenty-two years. In the midst of unimaginable atrocities, one man inspired Valladares to keep going—a man the prisoners called the "Brother of Faith."*

According to Valladares, the guards often beat the prisoners with bayonets and the blunt sides of machetes as the prisoners were herded from the labor fields back to their cells each day. One day, as the guards were corralling the prisoners, "they unleashed a hail of blows on the prisoners' backs," trying to get them to hurry back to their cells.

Suddenly, the guards began mercilessly beating the Brother of Faith. Valladares recalls:

There was not a trace of pain, not a tremble in his voice; it was as though it were not *his* back the machete was lashing over and over again, shredding his skin. The brilliant eyes of the Brother of Faith seemed to burn; his arms open to the sky seemed to draw down pardon for his exe-

cutioners. He was, at that instant, an incredible, supernatural, marvelous man.

Occasionally, the communists opened the cells and allowed the prisoners brief periods of "freedom" within the work camp. During those times, the Brother of Faith went from cell to cell, looking for sick men. He would take their clothes out to the prison yard and wash the filthy, ragged clothing in a basin.

The Brother of Faith often ignored his own welfare to serve his fellow prisoners. Valladares writes:

If some exhausted or sick prisoner fell behind in his work, the Brother of Faith would turn up, and help catch the man up on his work, preventing him from a brutal beating. When one of the guards would walk

up behind him and hit him, usually for no reason at all, the Brother of Faith would turn around, stand straight up, look right into that guard's eyes and say, "May God pardon you."

The self-effacing servant-hood demonstrated by the Brother of Faith in the worst of conditions is the sort of sacrificial service Jesus expects from you, too. Hopefully, your circumstances are better than those of Christians in countries where persecution of believers is common. That does not mean, however, that your mandate to serve others diminishes; on the contrary, it increases! To whom much is given, much is required.

The ways in which you can serve others as Jesus did are numerous. Jesus gave us a variety of examples, some of which are recorded in Matthew 8:1—9:38. Let's take a look.

WHAT IT MEANS TO BE LIKE JESUS

Jesus indicated that those who follow Him will become like Him (Matt. 10:25). What does it mean to **"be like Jesus"** *in today's complex world? Matthew paints eight portraits of what Christlikeness looks like, including:*

#7: To Be Like Jesus Means TO SERVE OTHERS

The Sermon on the Mount (Matt. 5–7) was immediately followed by "deeds in the valley" (Matt. 8–9). Christlike values lead to servant actions—and it was obedient action that Jesus cared about, not just sermonizing (7:21–29). Jesus modeled how to *do* the will of God by actively serving more than 25 different people (chs. 8–9). These included such undesirables as lepers, an officer of the Roman occupation troops, the sick, the demon-possessed, cave dwellers, tax collectors, and a diseased, outcast woman. If we want to be like Jesus, we need to befriend those who are weak, under oppression, or without Christ. Like Him, we need to become "a friend of sinners" (Matt. 11:19). He offered much more than religious information—He served them.

 Matthew 8:1—9:38

¹When He had come down from the mountain, great multitudes followed Him. ²And behold, a leper came and worshiped Him, saying, "Lord, if You are willing, You can make me clean."

³Then Jesus put out *His* hand and touched him, saying, "I am willing; be cleansed." Immediately his leprosy was cleansed.

⁴And Jesus said to him, "See that you tell no one; but go your way, show yourself to the priest, and offer the gift that Moses commanded, as a testimony to them."

⁵Now when Jesus had entered Capernaum, a centurion came to Him, pleading with Him, ⁶saying, "Lord, my servant is lying at home paralyzed, dreadfully tormented."

⁷And Jesus said to him, "I will come and heal him."

⁸The centurion answered and said, "Lord, I am not worthy that You should come under my roof. But only speak a word, and my servant will be healed. ⁹For I also am a man under authority, having soldiers under me. And I say to this *one,* 'Go,' and he goes; and to another, 'Come,' and he comes; and to my servant, 'Do this,' and he does it."

¹⁰When Jesus heard *it,* He marveled, and said to those who followed, "Assuredly, I say to you, I have not found such great faith, not even in Israel!

¹¹And I say to you that many will come from east and west, and sit down with Abraham, Isaac, and Jacob in the kingdom of heaven. ¹²But the sons of the kingdom will be cast out into outer darkness. There will be weeping and gnashing of teeth." ¹³Then Jesus said to the centurion, "Go your way; and as you have believed, *so* let it be done for you." And his servant was healed that same hour.

¹⁴Now when Jesus had come into Peter's house, He saw his wife's mother lying sick with a fever. ¹⁵So He touched her hand, and the fever left her. And she arose and served them.

¹⁶When evening had come, they brought to Him many who were demon-possessed. And He cast out the spirits with a word, and healed all who were sick, ¹⁷that it might be fulfilled which was spoken by Isaiah the prophet, saying:

"He Himself took our infirmities
And bore *our* sicknesses."

¹⁸And when Jesus saw great multitudes about Him, He gave a command to depart to the other side. ¹⁹Then a certain scribe came and said to Him, "Teacher, I will follow You wherever You go."

²⁰And Jesus said to him, "Foxes have holes

continued

continued

and birds of the air *have* nests, but the Son of Man has nowhere to lay *His* head."

21Then another of His disciples said to Him, "Lord, let me first go and bury my father."

22But Jesus said to him, "Follow Me, and let the dead bury their own dead."

23Now when He got into a boat, His disciples followed Him. 24And suddenly a great tempest arose on the sea, so that the boat was covered with the waves. But He was asleep. 25Then His disciples came to *Him* and awoke Him, saying, "Lord, save us! We are perishing!"

26But He said to them, "Why are you fearful, O you of little faith?" Then He arose and rebuked the winds and the sea, and there was a great calm. 27So the men marveled, saying, "Who can this be, that even the winds and the sea obey Him?"

28When He had come to the other side, to the country of the Gergesenes, there met Him two demon-possessed *men,* coming out of the tombs, exceedingly fierce, so that no one could pass that way. 29And suddenly they cried out, saying, "What have we to do with You, Jesus, You Son of God? Have You come here to torment us before the time?"

30Now a good way off from them there was a herd of many swine feeding. 31So the demons begged Him, saying, "If You cast us out, permit us to go away into the herd of swine."

32And He said to them, "Go." So when they had come out, they went into the herd of swine. And suddenly the whole herd of swine ran violently down the steep place into the sea, and perished in the water.

33Then those who kept *them* fled; and they went away into the city and told everything, including what *had happened* to the demon-possessed *men.* 34And behold, the whole city came out to meet Jesus. And when they saw Him, they begged *Him* to depart from their region.

CHAPTER 9

1So He got into a boat, crossed over, and came to His own city. 2Then behold, they brought to Him a paralytic lying on a bed. When Jesus saw their faith, He said to the paralytic, "Son, be of good cheer; your sins are forgiven you."

3And at once some of the scribes said within themselves, "This Man blasphemes!"

4But Jesus, knowing their thoughts, said, "Why do you think evil in your hearts? 5For which is easier, to say, '*Your* sins are forgiven you,' or to say, 'Arise and walk'? 6But that you may know that the Son of Man has power on earth to forgive sins"—then He said to the paralytic, "Arise, take up your bed, and go to your house." 7And he arose and departed to his house.

8Now when the multitudes saw *it,* they marveled and glorified God, who had given such power to men.

9As Jesus passed on from there, He saw a man named Matthew sitting at the tax office. And He said to him, "Follow Me." So he arose and followed Him.

10Now it happened, as Jesus sat at the table in the house, *that* behold, many tax collectors and sinners came and sat down with Him and His disciples. 11And when the Pharisees saw *it,* they said to His disciples, "Why does your Teacher eat with tax collectors and sinners?"

12When Jesus heard *that,* He said to them, "Those who are well have no need of a physician, but those who are sick. 13But go and learn what *this* means: 'I desire mercy and not sacrifice.' For I did not come to call the righteous, but sinners, to repentance."

14Then the disciples of John came to Him, saying, "Why do we and the Pharisees fast often, but Your disciples do not fast?"

15And Jesus said to them, "Can the friends of the bridegroom mourn as long as the bridegroom is with them? But the days will come when the bridegroom will be taken away from them, and then they will fast. 16No one puts a piece of unshrunk cloth on an old garment; for the patch pulls away from the garment, and the tear is made worse. 17Nor do they put new wine into old wineskins, or else the wineskins break, the wine is

continued

continued

spilled, and the wineskins are ruined. But they put new wine into new wineskins, and both are preserved."

¹⁸While He spoke these things to them, behold, a ruler came and worshiped Him, saying, "My daughter has just died, but come and lay Your hand on her and she will live." ¹⁹So Jesus arose and followed him, and so *did* His disciples.

²⁰And suddenly, a woman who had a flow of blood for twelve years came from behind and touched the hem of His garment. ²¹For she said to herself, "If only I may touch His garment, I shall be made well." ²²But Jesus turned around, and when He saw her He said, "Be of good cheer, daughter; your faith has made you well." And the woman was made well from that hour.

²³When Jesus came into the ruler's house, and saw the flute players and the noisy crowd wailing, ²⁴He said to them, "Make room, for the girl is not dead, but sleeping." And they ridiculed Him. ²⁵But when the crowd was put outside, He went in and took her by the hand, and the girl arose. ²⁶And the report of this went out into all that land.

²⁷When Jesus departed from there, two blind men followed Him, crying out and saying, "Son of David, have mercy on us!"

²⁸And when He had come into the house, the blind men came to Him. And Jesus said to them, "Do you believe that I am able to do this?"

They said to Him, "Yes, Lord."

²⁹Then He touched their eyes, saying, "According to your faith let it be to you." ³⁰And their eyes were opened. And Jesus sternly warned them, saying, "See *that* no one knows *it.*" ³¹But when they had departed, they spread the news about Him in all that country.

³²As they went out, behold, they brought to Him a man, mute and demon-possessed. ³³And when the demon was cast out, the mute spoke. And the multitudes marveled, saying, "It was never seen like this in Israel!"

³⁴But the Pharisees said, "He casts out demons by the ruler of the demons."

³⁵Then Jesus went about all the cities and villages, teaching in their synagogues, preaching the gospel of the kingdom, and healing every sickness and every disease among the people. ³⁶But when He saw the multitudes, He was moved with compassion for them, because they were weary and scattered, like sheep having no shepherd. ³⁷Then He said to His disciples, "The harvest truly *is* plentiful, but the laborers *are* few. ³⁸Therefore pray the Lord of the harvest to send out laborers into His harvest."

---

1. It is relatively easy for us to serve someone we know and like. But Jesus also commands us to serve people with whom we ordinarily would have little in common. Who are some of the people (or groups of people) in your life who are most difficult for you to serve?

_____

_____

_____

_____

2. List one specific thing you can do to serve each of the people (or groups of people) you listed in question 1.

_____

_____

_____

_____

3. Which of Jesus' acts of service in Matthew 8:1—9:38 intrigues you the most?

_____

_____

_____

4. What do you think Jesus meant when He referred to the crowd as a field ripe for harvest (9:37–38)?

_____

_____

_____

◆ The Vanishing Virtue ◆

In the Bible, one of the best examples of service and humility was John the Baptist. When we think of him today, we often forget that John was Jesus' cousin. Like many cousins of the same age, John could have been competitive with Jesus. After all, John's ministry was a stunning success before Jesus even entered the public scene. People were traveling great distances to see and hear John the Baptist, and many became his disciples.

John could have easily kept the crowds' attention focused on himself, but he didn't. Instead, he pointed to Jesus and said, "Behold! The Lamb of God who takes away the sin of the world!" (John 1:29). John willingly told the people to look toward Jesus, not to himself.

So, what does humility have to do with serving others? Everything. Without an attitude of humility, your service will always be tainted by selfish motives. You may do the "right" things, but for the wrong reasons. Perhaps that is why the apostle Paul admonished the believers at Philippi: "Let nothing be done through selfish ambition or conceit, but in lowliness of mind let each esteem others better than himself" (Phil. 2:3). Paul told them to serve each other by following Christ's example.

HUMILITY—THE SCANDALOUS VIRTUE

By recommending *"lowliness of mind" (Phil. 2:3), Paul fired a broadside at the Philippian culture—and our own. Like us, the Greeks and Romans exalted the lifestyles of the rich and famous!*

Lowliness of mind? Who would want that? A "lowly" (or humble) person meant a slave—a servile, groveling, wretched individual. And for Paul to associate the word "lowly" with "mind" was a laughable contradiction: everyone assumed that lowly people had no intelligence, and everyone honored higher thinking and self-conceit.

The idea of humility seemed especially out of place in Philippi. The town hosted a Roman military colony by the pretentious-sounding name of *Colonia Augusta Julia Pilippensis.* Unlike other conquered towns, it enjoyed the *jus Italicum* (law of Italy), which made it a sort of small, self-governing version of the empire. Pride and self-importance were part and parcel of Philippian life in Paul's day.

Yet Paul insisted that Christians there cultivate humility—but not a grovelling, abject demeanor. No, biblical humility means not thinking of oneself more highly than is true (Rom. 12:3), but rather acknowledging

what one is—with all of one's strengths and weaknesses, pluses and minuses, successes and failures.

Far from self-loathing, real humility makes people so truthful that they don't hesitate, when necessary, to tell about even their good qualities.

Do you want true humility? It comes from seeing yourself in relation to God. No wonder, then, that this virtue ran counter to the Roman worldview. Their concept of a god was grossly similar to their concept of humanity, and the mythological Roman gods were hardly noble.

By contrast, Jesus praised the humble, "the poor in spirit," (literally, "the destitute," Matt. 5:3). What would that attitude look like? David expresses it in Psalm 39:4–6:

Lord, make me to know my end,
And what is the measure of my days,
That I may know how frail I am.
Indeed, You have made my days as handbreadths,

And my age is as nothing before You;
Certainly every man at his best state is but vapor.
Surely every man walks about like a shadow;
Surely they busy themselves in vain;
He heaps up riches,
And does not know who will gather them.

Likewise, the prophet Micah warns that humility is one of three main virtues that ought to govern our lives (Mic. 6:8):

He has shown you, O man, what is good;
And what does the Lord require of you
But to do justly,
To love mercy,
And to walk humbly with your God?

Humility is not an option for us as believers—it's an essential if we want to walk with God. Over and again, Scripture insists that we either walk humbly with Him, or not at all (Ps. 138:6; Is. 57:15; 1 Pet. 5:5–7). In short, a biblical lifestyle knows nothing of looking out chiefly for Number One. Just the opposite. With John the Baptist we need to say, "He must increase, but I must decrease" (John 3:30). ◆

> **Philippians 2:1-4**
>
> ¹Therefore if *there is* any consolation in Christ, if any comfort of love, if any fellowship of the Spirit, if any affection and mercy, ²fulfill my joy by being like-minded, having the same love, *being of* one accord, of one mind. ³Let nothing *be done* through selfish ambition or conceit, but in lowliness of mind let each esteem others better than himself. ⁴Let each of you look out not only for his own interests, but also for the interests of others.

1. When you hear someone described as being a humble person, what are some of your first thoughts or impressions?

_____

_____

_____

2. In Philippians 2:2, Paul lists four ways we can work toward spiritual unity with our "brothers and sisters in the Lord," and serve one another. Explain what each of Paul's points means to you.

_____

_____

_____

_____

3. How can you develop true humility?

_____

_____

_____

◆ What's a Christian to Do? ◆

As Jeff was closing the curtains, he happened to look out the window of his inner-city apartment. To his horror, Jeff saw a man with a gun mugging another man on the street below.

He stiffened with fear.

What should I do? Should I run downstairs and attempt to intervene? The guy does have a gun . . . maybe he would shoot the man he was mugging and me! Jeff screamed to himself.

He reached for the telephone and dialed 911. "There's a robbery taking place right now outside my apartment!" he blurted into the receiver.

"Calm down," said a voice on the other end of the line. "Where are you located?"

"I'm on the corner of . . ." Jeff's words were interrupted by the sound of a gunshot.

◆ ◆ ◆ ◆ ◆ ◆ ◆ ◆ ◆

It was late at night and the torrential downpour seemed as though it might never let up. Emily swerved her car to avoid hydroplaning in a large pool of water that was creeping ominously across the highway. Just as she jerked the steering wheel, Emily saw a drenched, disheveled young man sticking out his thumb as he stood forlornly beside the road. Emily looked into the rearview mirror for the shadowy figure.

"I can't believe anyone would be hitchhiking on a night like this," she said aloud, glancing in the mirror. *I know it is not smart to pick up a stranger—especially at this hour—but I hate to pass him by and leave him in this kind of weather,* she mused. *What should I do?*

◆ ◆ ◆ ◆ ◆ ◆ ◆ ◆ ◆

Indeed, what is a believer to do in the face of risky opportunities to help needy, hurting people? What would you have done, if you were:

*Jeff?*_____

_____

_____

*Emily?*_____

_____

_____

Jesus' love for us is unconditional; He does not say, "If you treat Me right, I will treat you right." Jesus wants us to love and serve those who are unloved and often ungrateful. He wants us to return good for evil. But how far should we go? When does reaching out in faith become an exercise in futility and foolishness? The answers may surprise you. ◆

RUNNING TO EXTREMES

Did Christ intend for us to take what He said in Luke 6:27–36 literally? It sounds noble to love our enemies, bless those who curse us, and pray for those who spite us. But what about physical abuse, robbery, or endless appeals for help (vv. 29–30)? Surely He didn't mean those words the way they sound. Or does Christianity encourage people to run to dangerous extremes?

It's legitimate to notice that Jesus often used hyperbole and stark contrasts in His comments here. So when we read Jesus' words today, it's easy to set up all kinds of exceptions and qualifications to soften them. But in the process, do we miss His point? Do we distort His message?

Jesus was not calling here for unhealthy responses, nor setting forth a political or social agenda, nor offering a statement of public policy, nor constructing a model for business and finance. Instead, He posed a tough challenge to His followers—to those "who hear" (v. 27): What difference does our faith make in the way we respond to people

continued

continued

in need? That's the key—our response to human need. That shows the true condition of our hearts. Do we respond to people as God Himself does, with mercy (v. 36)?

The test comes when we are faced with extremes. As Jesus pointed out, it's easy to love those who love us (v. 32). It's easy to give when we know we'll get back (v. 34). But God loves people who do not love Him, and gives to those who will never even thank Him, let alone give back to Him (v. 35).

Even God's enemies have needs that only He can meet. In His mercy, He meets those needs. Do we? When faced with people in genuine need, do we look only at their character, and base our response on that alone? Or do we look at their needs and do what we can to meet them?

We may question how far Jesus wants us to go in the various situations described in vv. 29–30. But we need never question how far God is willing to go to show mercy. That's what we need to take literally and imitate practically. ◆

 Luke 6:27–36

²⁷"But I say to you who hear: Love your enemies, do good to those who hate you, ²⁸bless those who curse you, and pray for those who spitefully use you. ²⁹To him who strikes you on the *one* cheek, offer the other also. And from him who takes away your cloak, do not withhold *your* tunic either. ³⁰Give to everyone who asks of you. And from him who takes away your goods do not ask *them* back. ³¹And just as you want men to do to you, you also do to them likewise.

³²"But if you love those who love you, what credit is that to you? For even sinners love those who love them. ³³And if you do good to those who do good to you, what credit is that to you? For even sinners do the same. ³⁴And if you lend *to those* from whom you hope to receive back, what credit is that to you? For even sinners lend to sinners to receive as much back. ³⁵But love your enemies, do good, and lend, hoping for nothing in return; and your reward will be great, and you will be sons of the Most High. For He is kind to the unthankful and evil. ³⁶Therefore be merciful, just as your Father also is merciful."

1. How does it make you feel when you see someone who needs your help? Check all that apply.

_____ Angry   _____ Indifferent
_____ Grieved   _____ Excited
_____ Depressed

2. What is the motivation behind the expressions described in Luke 6:32–34?

_____

_____

3. What does Jesus imply about us when we do good things from a similar motivation?

_____

_____

4. How can you prevent improper motivation from discrediting your service?

_____

_____

_____

_____

——◆ A Better Style of Leadership ◆——

Servant-leadership. *The two roles seem incompatible. How is it possible for a servant to be a leader? Better still, how can a leader be a servant?*

Leaders are frequently pampered, admired, and given the "red carpet treatment." Often, their quirks and uncomplimentary qualities are excused or ignored. After all, doesn't their gift of leadership make up for their propensity toward pride, egotism, and arrogance? Besides, if a leader is to get anything done, that person must be stubborn, opinionated, and outspoken—right?

Wrong! Throughout His life, Jesus modeled a different kind of leadership. Although He deserved the adulation of His disciples, He willingly humbled Himself before them, patiently taught them, provided for their needs, and eventually gave His life on their behalf.

Jesus was establishing a pattern for His disciples to follow after He was gone. He fully expected His followers to be servant-leaders, willing to humbly serve God, each other, and the world. He expects the same from us today.

◆ ◆ ◆ ◆ ◆ ◆ ◆ ◆ ◆

THE ORDER OF THE TOWEL

Leadership is a fascinating topic. Business books offer models of leadership as diverse as Attila the Hun, Oriental warlords, and Abraham Lincoln. But Jesus painted a different picture of leadership.

As He wrapped up His work, Jesus held a dinner for His closest associates. Instead of delivering a state-of-the-union address or naming a successor, He chose to leave His seat at the head of the table and pick up some household servant's equipment—a basin of water and a towel. He then washed the feet of every person at the table—even Judas, His betrayer (John 13:1–20). Footwashing was usually performed by household servants as an act of hospitality to weary, dusty guests. Leaders and hosts did not stoop to such a menial task. But Jesus did.

Seated once again at the table, the Lord asked whether His followers understood what He had done (John 13:12). He then exhorted them to adopt the same posture of serving others, thereby following His example. He assured them that they would be blessed if they did (vv. 15–17).

Jesus still calls believers today to become members of the "Order of the Towel." As Christ's followers, we need to lead others by serving them.

A MODEL OF SERVANT-LEADERSHIP

When Jesus washed His disciples' feet (John 13:3–5), He demonstrated a fundamental principle that He regularly stressed to His followers: To lead others, one must serve others. This is as true in public life and the business world as it is in the church. No number of corporate memos or rah-rah speeches exhorting workers to commit themselves to an organization or its clients will have as powerful an impact as a person of authority modeling consistently and clearly the attitude of a servant: placing others' needs before one's own, committing oneself to doing concrete things to meet those needs, and looking for neither favors nor reciprocity from the people one serves.

John 13:1–20

[1]Now before the Feast of the Passover, when Jesus knew that His hour had come that He should depart from this world to the Father, having loved His own who were in the world, He loved them to the end.

[2]And supper being ended, the devil having already put it into the heart of Judas Iscariot, Simon's *son,* to betray Him, [3]Jesus, knowing that the Father had given all things into His hands, and that He had come from God and was going to God, [4]rose from supper and laid aside His garments, took a towel and girded Himself. [5]After that, He poured water into a basin and began to wash the disciples' feet, and to wipe *them* with the towel with which He was girded. [6]Then He came to Simon Peter. And *Peter* said to Him, "Lord, are You washing my feet?"

[7]Jesus answered and said to him, "What I am doing you do not understand now, but you will know after this."

[8]Peter said to Him, "You shall never wash my feet!"

Jesus answered him, "If I do not wash you, you have no part with Me."

[9]Simon Peter said to Him, "Lord, not my feet only, but also *my* hands and *my* head!"

[10]Jesus said to him, "He who is bathed needs only to wash *his* feet, but is completely clean; and you are clean, but not all of you." [11]For He knew who would betray Him; therefore He said, "You are not all clean."

[12]So when He had washed their feet, taken His garments, and sat down again, He said to them, "Do you know what I have done to you? [13]You call Me Teacher and Lord, and you say well, for *so* I am. [14]If I then, *your* Lord and Teacher, have washed your feet, you also ought to wash one another's feet. [15]For I have given you an example, that you should do as I have done to you. [16]Most assuredly, I say to you, a servant is not greater than his master; nor is he who is sent greater than he who sent him. [17]If you know these things, blessed are you if you do them.

[18]"I do not speak concerning all of you. I know whom I have chosen; but that the Scripture may be fulfilled, 'He who eats bread with Me has lifted up his heel against Me.' [19]Now I tell you before it comes, that when it does come to pass, you may believe that I am *He.* [20]Most assuredly, I say to you, he who receives whomever I send receives Me; and he who receives Me receives Him who sent Me."

1a. Think of a contemporary leader who models servant-leadership. What qualities do you admire in this person?

_____

_____

_____

_____

1b. On a scale of one to ten, how well are you incorporating those qualities in your life?

Not Very Well   Extremely Well

1   2   3   4   5   6   7   8   9   10

2. In John 13:1–20, Jesus washed the feet of His disciples, including Judas, who was about to betray Jesus. What does Christ's willingness to wash Judas' feet say to you about serving those people who betray or hurt you?

_____

_____

_____

_____

3. Why do you think Peter was so repulsed at the idea of Jesus' washing the disciples' feet?

_____

_____

_____

_____

4. What do you think is the meaning of Jesus' conversation with Peter in verses 8–10?

_____

_____

_____

Jesus calls us to serve fellow believers, our family members, our communities, and the world. That is not an easy job description. The job is especially difficult because putting someone else's needs before your own often goes against human nature.

But God reveals something radically different from our contemporary success stories. The Bible says that Jesus Christ, King of kings and Lord of lords, humbled Himself and became the servant of all. Now, He asks us to do the same.

Are you reluctant to humble yourself, fearing that if you place others' needs before your own, you will condemn yourself to a life of meaningless obscurity? Don't be! Jesus does not take a "somebody" and transform that person into a "nobody." On the contrary, He loves to make "somebodies" out of "nobodies."

Being a leader in God's eyes is not contingent upon your personality or talents. If that were the case, few of the early disciples would have qualified for service. Yet Jesus taught His disciples how to be good followers and that prepared them to be good leaders. In our next chapter, you will discover how you, too, can make that same transition!

ENCOURAGING LEADERS

CHAPTER 12

A fanciful legend recounts a conversation between Jesus and the archangel, Gabriel, following Christ's return to heaven after His ministry on earth. Gabriel listened intently as Jesus described the people He had healed, the crowds to whom He had preached, how He had suffered and died on the cross, and what it was like to rise from the dead. Jesus concluded His account by telling Gabriel about His desire that people everywhere—in every age—should hear the gospel, believe it, and come to know Him.

Gabriel agreed, but he had a question. "Do the people on earth know how much You love them and what You did for them?"

"No, not yet," Jesus replied. "Right now only a small group of people in Palestine know, and most of them don't fully understand yet."

Gabriel became curious and asked, "Then what are Your plans to let everyone know about Your love for them?"

Jesus responded, "I've asked Peter, James, John, and a few more friends to tell other people about Me."

"But, with all due respect," Gabriel politely protested, "do You really think those few friends can communicate Your message to the entire world?"

Jesus replied, "Sure. My plan is for those who have heard the gospel to tell others, and they will tell even more folks. People from every na-tion, tribe, and tongue will learn about My love for them, and they will believe."

Gabriel was skeptical; he gently broached the subject again. "What if Peter, James, and John get tired of telling others about You? What if the people who come after them don't believe or don't take the gospel seriously? What will happen if twenty centuries from now believers get lazy and quit telling the good news of Your love? What is Plan B?"

Jesus smiled slightly at Gabriel and replied, "I have no other plans, Gabriel. There is no Plan B if My friends fail to share the gospel. I am counting on them."

* * * * * * * * *

Twenty-one centuries later, Jesus' plan to reach the world with His message of love, forgiveness, and reconciliation to God remains the same. And, He is counting on us to continue to lead others.

WHAT IT MEANS TO BE LIKE JESUS

Jesus indicated that those who follow Him will become like Him (Matt. 10:25). What does it mean to **"be like Jesus"** in today's complex world? Matthew paints eight portraits of what Christlikeness looks like, including affirming other leaders.

#8: To Be Like Jesus Means TO AFFIRM OTHER LEADERS

Jesus invested Himself in the development of other people, particularly the Twelve. He gave them responsibility and authority, resisting the temptation to get the job done "right" by doing it Himself. In doing so, He accepted the risk that they might fail. Of

continued

145

continued
course, He gave them adequate preparation before sending them out, and on their return He affirmed them on their successful comple- **tion of the mission. Jesus calls us to help others grow. If we want to be like Him, we will share the joys and risks of working together with our brothers and sisters.**

 Matthew 10:1–42

¹And when He had called His twelve disciples to *Him,* He gave them power *over* unclean spirits, to cast them out, and to heal all kinds of sickness and all kinds of disease. ²Now the names of the twelve apostles are these: first, Simon, who is called Peter, and Andrew his brother; James the *son* of Zebedee, and John his brother; ³Philip and Bartholomew; Thomas and Matthew the tax collector; James the *son* of Alphaeus, and Lebbaeus, whose surname was Thaddaeus; ⁴Simon the Cananite, and Judas Iscariot, who also betrayed Him.

⁵These twelve Jesus sent out and commanded them, saying: "Do not go into the way of the Gentiles, and do not enter a city of the Samaritans. ⁶But go rather to the lost sheep of the house of Israel. ⁷And as you go, preach, saying, 'The kingdom of heaven is at hand.' ⁸Heal the sick, cleanse the lepers, raise the dead, cast out demons. Freely you have received, freely give. ⁹Provide neither gold nor silver nor copper in your money belts, ¹⁰nor bag for *your* journey, nor two tunics, nor sandals, nor staffs; for a worker is worthy of his food.

¹¹"Now whatever city or town you enter, inquire who in it is worthy, and stay there till you go out. ¹²And when you go into a household, greet it. ¹³If the household is worthy, let your peace come upon it. But if it is not worthy, let your peace return to you. ¹⁴And whoever will not receive you nor hear your words, when you depart from that house or city, shake off the dust from your feet. ¹⁵Assuredly, I say to you, it will be more tolerable for the land of Sodom and Gomorrah in the day of judgment than for that city!

¹⁶"Behold, I send you out as sheep in the midst of wolves. Therefore be wise as serpents and harmless as doves. ¹⁷But beware of men, for they will deliver you up to councils and scourge you in their synagogues. ¹⁸You will be brought before governors and kings for My sake, as a testimony to them and to the Gentiles. ¹⁹But when they deliver you up, do not worry about how or what you should speak. For it will be given to you in that hour what you should speak; ²⁰for it is not you who speak, but the Spirit of your Father who speaks in you.

²¹"Now brother will deliver up brother to death, and a father *his* child; and children will rise up against parents and cause them to be put to death. ²²And you will be hated by all for My name's sake. But he who endures to the end will be saved. ²³When they persecute you in this city, flee to another. For assuredly, I say to you, you will not have gone through the cities of Israel before the Son of Man comes.

²⁴"A disciple is not above *his* teacher, nor a servant above his master. ²⁵It is enough for a disciple that he be like his teacher, and a servant like his master. If they have called the master of the house Beelzebub, how much more *will they call* those of his household! ²⁶Therefore do not fear them. For there is nothing covered that will not be revealed, and hidden that will not be known.

²⁷"Whatever I tell you in the dark, speak in the light; and what you hear in the ear, preach on the housetops. ²⁸And do not fear those who kill the body but cannot kill the soul. But rather fear Him who is able to destroy both soul and body in hell. ²⁹Are not two sparrows sold for a copper coin? And not one of them falls to the ground apart from your Father's will. ³⁰But the very hairs of your head are all numbered. ³¹Do not fear therefore; you are of more value than many sparrows.

continued

continued

³²"Therefore whoever confesses Me before men, him I will also confess before My Father who is in heaven. ³³But whoever denies Me before men, him I will also deny before My Father who is in heaven.

³⁴"Do not think that I came to bring peace on earth. I did not come to bring peace but a sword. ³⁵For I have come to 'set a man against his father, a daughter against her mother, and a daughter-in-law against her mother-in-law'; ³⁶and 'a man's enemies will be those of his *own household.*' ³⁷He who loves father or mother more than Me is not worthy of Me. And he who loves son or daughter more than Me is not worthy of Me. ³⁸And he who does not take his cross and follow after Me is not worthy of Me. ³⁹He who finds his life will lose it, and he who loses his life for My sake will find it.

⁴⁰"He who receives you receives Me, and he who receives Me receives Him who sent Me. ⁴¹He who receives a prophet in the name of a prophet shall receive a prophet's reward. And he who receives a righteous man in the name of a righteous man shall receive a righteous man's reward. ⁴²And whoever gives one of these little ones only a cup of cold *water* in the name of a disciple, assuredly, I say to you, he shall by no means lose his reward."

1. In what or whom are you investing for your future?

_____ Stocks and bonds
_____ My children
_____ An individual retirement fund
_____ My career
_____ My church
_____ Nothing

2. Jesus invested a lot of time in His first twelve disciples. What risks do you think He was taking by making such a large investment in so few followers?

_____

_____

_____

_____

3. Why did Jesus instruct the Twelve not to take necessities, such as money, extra clothes, and shoes, on their journey (Matt. 10:8–10)?

_____

_____

_____

_____

_____

4. In Matthew 10:25, Jesus suggests that His followers should be like Him. What are you doing to be more like Jesus in your leadership style?

_____

_____

——◆ God Wants Leaders, Not Dictators ◆——

In his book, *13 Fatal Errors Managers Make,* W. Steven Brown relates a story about an overzealous, egocentric manager who attempted to flaunt his authority in a meeting with a group of his subordinates. Brown writes:

> Roughly thirty minutes after the meeting's start, the back door of the room opened, and I saw a great shock of silver hair. A big, handsome man in his mid-sixties entered. When he realized he was late, he scrunched up, making himself as small as possible, and tiptoed over to a chair. He prepared to sit down when the man running the meeting stopped him with the question, "What is your name, sir?"
>
> "Peters, sir. I'm awfully sorry I'm late."
>
> "Mr. Peters, what time was this meeting called for?"
>
> "Nine o'clock, sir."
>
> "Mr. Peters, do you have a military background?"
>
> "Yes, I do, sir."
>
> "Mr. Peters, in the military, if you arrived at nine-thirty for a nine o'clock meeting, what would have happened?"
>
> With that Peters drew himself up to his full height and smiled, "When I entered, everyone would have stood, saluted, and said, 'Good morning, sir.' "

Peters was a retired general!

◆ ◆ ◆ ◆ ◆ ◆ ◆ ◆ ◆

Unlike General Peters' boss, the apostle Paul knew how to exercise authority without misusing it. Even when he had to rebuke his subordinates or write letters of correction to various churches, the apostle always sought to build up his fellow believers, not to embarrass them or tear them down. You can do the same to those over whom you exercise authority, seeking to encourage those who follow you. ◆

SPIRITUAL AUTHORITY

If you exercise leadership among other believers, you'll want to carefully study Paul's comment about his authority (2 Cor. 13:10). Like many of us, Paul liked to be in charge, and he felt frustrated when people failed to follow his lead, as the Corinthians had. As an apostle, he had spiritual authority over them, which at times led him to deal severely with them (1 Cor. 4:21; 5:5; Titus 1:13).

But it's important to notice how Paul exercised his authority, especially as he grew older in the faith. He didn't lord it over others or try to use his authority to personal advantage. Nor did he abuse his power by using it to work out his own anger. Instead, he recognized that spiritual authority is given "for edification and not for destruction" (2 Cor. 10:8; 13:10), for building others up, not for tearing them down.

Is that how you use your position and authority? Do you exercise leadership in order to accomplish the best interests of those who follow you? As they carry out your directives, are they built up in Christ, or torn down?

2 Corinthians 13:9–10

⁹For we are glad when we are weak and you are strong. And this also we pray, that you may be made complete. ¹⁰Therefore I write these things being absent, lest being present I should use sharpness, according to the authority which the Lord has given me for edification and not for destruction.

1. Why do you think leaders sometimes abuse their power?

_____

_____

_____

2. Think of a time when one of your leaders used authority for personal advantage. How did it make you feel?

Angry　　　Manipulated　　　Helpless　　　Confused　　　Indifferent

3. Think of some people who look to you for leadership (for instance, your family, a young child, coworkers). How do you usually respond when you must correct their actions?

_____

_____

_____

4. If those who follow you incorporate your methods of leadership, will they grow more or less like Jesus?

_____

_____

◆ Faithful Followers ◆

"Hey, Pete! Why don't we leave the office a little early this afternoon and go hit a few golf balls?"

"Yeah, right. Sam, you know Mr. Jones asked me to run the sales figures for this quarter."

"Sure, I know," Sam answered, raising his eyebrows as he spoke. "But Jones is at the home office and won't be back until Monday. As long as you get the figures done before then, he'll never know the difference. Come on, look outside. It is a gorgeous day to be on the golf course. Let's go!"

What would you do if you were Pete?

_____

_____

_____

◆ ◆ ◆ ◆ ◆ ◆ ◆ ◆ ◆

Jesus wants His followers to be consistently faithful to Him. He expects both those who exercise authority and those who are under authority to be diligently working and ready to meet Christ without embarrass- *ment when He returns. In the meantime, we can practice our faithfulness to Christ by modeling faithfulness in all of our other relationships—including our obedience and loyalty to our supervisors in the workplace.* ◆

AUTHORITY AND RESPONSIBILITY

All of us must deal with authority and responsibility. The parables Jesus told (Luke 12:35–48) talk about the believer's faithfulness to God. But they also remind us of faithful conduct on the job.

To be sure, our work relationships are more complicated—and civilized—than those between slaves and masters. But in light of the principles raised in this passage, we might ask: Are we as productive when our supervisors are gone as when they are looking over us? Do we try to anticipate their needs and desires, or do we wait until told what to do? Do we pray for our bosses and the work we do under them?

Jesus has a high regard for faithfulness. In this passage He challenges us to carry out our spiritual responsibilities in a faithful, diligent way. But clearly we need to fulfill our everyday work responsibilities with the same reliable, faithful spirit.

 Luke 12:35–48

35"Let your waist be girded and *your* lamps burning; 36and you yourselves be like men who wait for their master, when he will return from the wedding, that when he comes and knocks they may open to him immediately. 37Blessed *are* those servants whom the master, when he comes, will find watching. Assuredly, I say to you that he will gird himself and have them sit down *to eat,* and will come and serve them. 38And if he should come in the second watch, or come in the third watch, and find *them* so, blessed are those servants. 39But know this, that if the master of the house had known what hour the thief would come, he would have watched and not allowed his house to be broken into. 40Therefore you also be ready, for the Son of Man is coming at an hour you do not expect."

41Then Peter said to Him, "Lord, do You speak this parable *only* to us, or to all *people?*"

42And the Lord said, "Who then is that faithful and wise steward, whom *his* master will make ruler over his household, to give *them their* portion of food in due season? 43Blessed *is* that servant whom his master will find so doing when he comes. 44Truly, I say to you that he will make him ruler over all that he has. 45But if that servant says in his heart, 'My master is delaying his coming,' and begins to beat the male and female servants, and to eat and drink and be drunk, 46the master of that servant will come on a day when he is not looking for *him,* and at an hour when he is not aware, and will cut him in two and appoint *him* his portion with the unbelievers. 47And that servant who knew his master's will, and did not prepare *himself* or do according to his will, shall be beaten with many *stripes.* 48But he who did not know, yet committed things deserving of stripes, shall be beaten with few. For everyone to whom much is given, from him much will be required; and to whom much has been committed, of him they will ask the more."

1. Why do you think Jesus never told us the exact date He would return to earth?

_____

_____

_____

_____

2. Why is it so awful to know your leader's wishes and not follow through with pleasing that leader (Luke 12:47–48)?

_____

_____

_____

3. In Luke 12:48, Jesus said, "For everyone to whom much is given, from him much will be required." How does this apply to your life?

_____

_____

_____

_____

——◆ Leaders Need Love, Too! ◆——

"Christina! Can't you do anything right?" Christina's boss chided. "I said I wanted the Smith file, not the Roberts file. Can't you hear?"

"Yes, Mrs. Lambert. I'm sorry. But I'm certain that I heard you request the Roberts file."

Mrs. Lambert slumped back in her plush leather chair.

She sighed heavily and said, "Oh, maybe I did. I'm not sure what I am doing today."

Christina stood at the door, awaiting further instructions from her boss, but Mrs. Lambert was simply staring into space. "Excuse me . . . Mrs. Lambert, are you feeling okay?" Christina ventured.

"Huh? Oh, yes; I'm fine, Christina. Thank you. And I'm sorry for snapping at you. I've been under quite a bit of pressure lately."

"Is there anything I can do?" Christina asked.

"No, not unless you are a miracle worker," Mrs. Lambert replied. Then Mrs. Lambert, the normally consummate business executive, began to cry.

Christina was stunned. "Mrs. Lambert! What is wrong? Shall I call a doctor?"

Mrs. Lambert quickly regained her composure. "No, no, Christina; I'm fine. Really. I guess everything is just getting to me. You may have heard that my husband was hospitalized last week. The doctors say it is cancer, and it is already in the latter stages. The doctors don't offer much hope."

"No, Mrs. Lambert. I hadn't heard that at all . . ."

"Now—today—the home office has sent word that they are closing our division of the company. We're not competitive enough, they say. What do these people expect? They cut our staff, slice our budget, siphon off our best people into other parts of the company,

and then complain that we are not competitive! It's a joke!"

Christina looked at her boss's face. It was as if it were the first time she ever really looked at Mrs. Lambert. Ordinarily, Christina saw her boss as the superhuman, cold-hearted, manipulative business executive. Now, for the first time, Christina saw her boss as a real person with genuine hurts, fears, and problems like everyone else. Christina felt compassion for Mrs. Lambert the person.

Mrs. Lambert dabbed her eyes with a handkerchief. "I'm sorry to have unloaded on you, Christina. Like I said, there's nothing you can do, unless you can work miracles." She attempted a faint smile.

Christina thought for a moment, then said softly, "Per-

haps we can all work together to prove to the home office how valuable our work is. None of us knew things were so serious. Come on, we've got work to do!"

◆ ◆ ◆ ◆ ◆ ◆ ◆ ◆ ◆

Being a leader is not an easy role. Other people constantly look to the leader for strength, encouragement, and answers that the leader may not have. It is a rare—but commendable—quality when a leader is willing to be vulnerable and say, "I'm hurting, too. I need your help." The apostle Paul was that type of person; he was able to honestly share his heart without compromising or diminishing the respect of those who followed him. Paul's openness actually caused his followers to love, appreciate, and encourage him even more. ◆

ENCOURAGING THE BOSS

Separation from close friends can bring feelings of loneliness and loss, especially when one is facing disappointment or failure. Paul felt that way in Athens. Despite his strident efforts to present and defend the gospel, he met with only lackluster response from the Athenians (Acts 17:16–34). Not surprisingly, his thoughts turned toward the Thessalonians with whom he felt an unusually deep bond (1 Thess. 2:8; 2:17—3:1).

Anxious for news, Paul sent his valuable associate Timothy north for a visit (3:2). The young man's report buoyed Paul up. Even as one city was resisting Christ, another was responding to Him in powerful and encouraging ways (3:6–10).

Paul's emotional honesty here is refreshing and instructive. Rather than deny or spiritualize his pain, he acknowledged it and took action. He needed the warm affection of the Thessalonians and especially the capable companionship of Timothy. Rather than live as a "Lone Ranger Christian," Paul stayed connected to other believers and relied on them for insight, encouragement, and support. In this way he honored a basic principle of Christian community (Heb. 10:24–25).

Does your supervisor need encouragement, affirmation, or help in keeping the big picture? Often when people are under great stress or feeling a sense of failure, the only thing they hear is what's wrong. Can you encourage yours with a word about what is *right*?

1 Thessalonians 3:1–10

¹Therefore, when we could no longer endure it, we thought it good to be left in Athens alone, ²and sent Timothy, our brother and minister of God, and our fellow laborer in the gospel of Christ, to establish you and encourage you concerning your faith, ³that no one should be shaken by these afflictions; for you yourselves know that we are appointed to this. ⁴For, in fact, we told you before when we were with you that we would suffer tribulation, just as it happened, and you know. ⁵For this reason, when I could no longer endure it, I sent to know your faith, lest by some means the tempter had tempted you, and our labor might be in vain.

⁶But now that Timothy has come to us from you, and brought us good news of your faith and love, and that you always have good remembrance of us, greatly desiring to see us, as we also *to see* you— ⁷therefore, brethren, in all our affliction and distress we were comforted concerning you by your faith. ⁸For now we live, if you stand fast in the Lord.

⁹For what thanks can we render to God for you, for all the joy with which we rejoice for your sake before our God, ¹⁰night and day praying exceedingly that we may see your face and perfect what is lacking in your faith?

1a. When you think about how your boss or a spiritual or political leader is performing, do you tend to focus on the positive or the negative things that person does?

_____

1b. List three positive things your boss or leader has done recently.

_____

_____

_____

2. Although the apostle Paul was a strong, confident leader, you can see in 1 Thessalonians 3:1–10 that he also had a sensitive side. Like a parent waiting to hear news about a child, Paul was concerned for the spiritual well-being of the new believers at Thessalonica. How has your boss or leader revealed concern for you or your coworkers?

_____

_____

3. What do you think Paul meant when he said, "For now we live, if you stand fast in the Lord" (1 Thess. 3:8)?

_____

_____

◆ When You Must Disobey Your Leaders ◆

It happens to almost everyone at some point: You are in conflict with your boss or another leader, and that person demands that you do something which contradicts your beliefs as a Christian. What do you do?

The apostle Peter and some of the other early believers were faced with such a situation. The high priest and his Sadducean friends ordered the early believers to stop talking about Jesus. In fact, they went so far as to have the believers locked up and guarded.

This did not stop these faithful Christians, though. Once they were set free, they went right back to the temple to continue spreading the good news of Christ.

Would we be able to do the same thing? Faced with fierce opposition, are you bold enough to obey God rather than men?

"WE OUGHT TO OBEY GOD RATHER THAN MEN"

What should Christians do when faced with a conflict between human authority and God's authority? Notice what Peter and the other apostles did (Acts 5:22–32):

(1) Their aim was to serve and glorify God. They were not motivated by ego or out to protect their own power.

(2) Their point of disobedience was specific and particular. They did not resist the authority of the Jewish council in total.

(3) They approached the situation with a spirit of submissiveness toward both the council and God. They did not harbor rebellious anger toward authority in general.

(4) They delivered a positive, factual message about God's plan and power in loving truth. They did not slander or show disrespect to their superiors.

(5) They accepted the cost of being loyal to the truth without rancor or bitterness.

 Acts 5:17–32

17Then the high priest rose up, and all those who *were* with him (which is the sect of the Sadducees), and they were filled with indignation, 18and laid their hands on the apostles and put them in the common prison. 19But at night an angel of the Lord opened the prison doors and brought them out, and said, 20"Go, stand in the temple and speak to the people all the words of this life."

21And when they heard *that*, they entered the temple early in the morning and taught. But the high priest and those with him came and called the council together, with all the elders of the children of Israel, and sent to the prison to have them brought.

22But when the officers came and did not find them in the prison, they returned and reported, 23saying, "Indeed we found the prison shut securely, and the guards standing outside before the doors; but when we opened them, we found no one inside!" 24Now when the high priest, the captain of the temple, and the chief priests heard these things, they wondered what the outcome would be. 25So one came and told them, saying, "Look, the men whom you put in prison are standing in the temple and teaching the people!"

26Then the captain went with the officers and brought them without violence, for they feared the

continued

continued

people, lest they should be stoned. ²⁷And when they had brought them, they set *them* before the council. And the high priest asked them, ²⁸saying, "Did we not strictly command you not to teach in this name? And look, you have filled Jerusalem with your doctrine, and intend to bring this Man's blood on us!"

²⁹But Peter and the *other* apostles answered and said: "We ought to obey God rather than men. ³⁰The God of our fathers raised up Jesus whom you murdered by hanging on a tree. ³¹Him God has exalted to His right hand *to be* Prince and Savior, to give repentance to Israel and forgiveness of sins. ³²And we are His witnesses to these things, and *so* also is the Holy Spirit whom God has given to those who obey Him."

1a. Describe a time when you experienced conflict between obeying your boss (or another leader who had authority over you) and obeying God.

_____

_____

_____

1b. In the situation in 1a, how did you respond and what factors influenced your decision?

_____

_____

_____

2. In your opinion, when is it a Christian's responsibility to become involved in civil disobedience?

_____

_____

_____

3. What factors do you think caused Peter—the same disciple who denied knowing Jesus to a servant girl (John 18:15–27)—to have such bold confidence before the high priest?

_____

_____

_____

_____

The message resonates throughout the New Testament: If you want to be a good leader then you must first learn how to follow and to serve. Anyone who refuses to serve, will be a poor leader. Power and authority in the hands of someone who does not have a servant's heart will eventually become a corrupting influence. History contains many examples of what happens when selfish people have attempted to use their power or position to manipulate others.

On the other hand, when people lead as Jesus did, the world is always changed for the better. People's lives are affected positively when they see genuine, godly leadership lived out in daily life. Perhaps that is why God instructs us to obey, encourage, respect, and pray for our leaders.

Even when you cannot respect an individual in power because of sin, compromise, or foolishness, you should still respect the position that person holds. When it becomes necessary to raise your voice or take a stand in opposition to compromising authority, God will provide you with the proper plan for doing so.

As His representative, God calls you to take the gospel into the world and show people that there is a better way to live, which begins by trusting Jesus. As we represent Jesus to the world, He calls us to break cycles of hatred and replace them with His love. We are to break down walls of prejudice and express forgiveness and a willingness to work together.

Whether we lead or follow, we are to live not by the values of this present world, but by the principles revealed in God's Word. As we do, we will continue to experience the Word of God in our own lives, and we will make God's Word relevant to the world around us.

LIVING WITHIN THE BIG PICTURE

t's hard to believe that twelve chapters about putting God's Word to work in our lives have gone by so quickly! It has been challenging to look at life from God's perspective and to try to adopt this new outlook.

This chapter is intended to help you sum up what you've learned and put it all together in your heart and mind so you can "take it to the streets." Hopefully, as you have progressed through this book, you have obtained some fresh ideas about how your relationship with Christ can grow deeper, how your attitude about life can improve, and how your convictions can become clearer.

As you follow Christ, He will continue to guide you as long as you allow Him to work in and through you.

——◆ Getting the Big Picture ◆——

Perhaps you were surprised to discover in chapter 1 that following Jesus is not a part-time venture. God wants you to love and serve Him with all your being. Every area of your life should reflect your love for God.

Jesus came to earth to show us how to do just this. He lived a sinless life and then gave Himself as a sacrifice for our sins. That sacrifice makes it possible for us to have eternal life with Jesus.

God gave us the Bible so we would have a trustworthy standard of truth. He wanted us to know how to live our lives in a way that is pleasing to Him. As we learn to follow God's Word more closely, the people around us will notice. In fact, people will be watching us to see how Christians handle responsibilities and resources.

◆ ◆ ◆ ◆ ◆ ◆ ◆ ◆ ◆

1. What evidence do you have that Jesus has made a difference in your life?

_____

_____

2. What makes the Bible so different from all other books?

_____

_____

3. Why is it vital that we spread the gospel to the entire world?

_____

_____

———◆ Unfolding Faith ◆———

Today, most societal pressures to conform to a particular set of religious beliefs have been removed. In some circles, you may even be thought less of for being a Christian. Why then, would anyone want to trust someone whom he has never actually seen or heard? When you consider the strong commitment it takes to follow Jesus, you may have wondered, What's in it for me?

Such questions deserve more than trite, superficial responses. In chapter 2, we attempted to discover honest answers. We recognized that faith unfolds slowly. Most people do not wake up one morning and say, "Ahh, it's a beautiful day. I think I'll become a Christian!" Usually, developing faith is a process, not a one-time event.

People often begin this journey by asking, "How can faith in Jesus meet my needs?" Such seeking should never be discouraged nor discounted. Many biblical characters came to Jesus in order to have their immediate needs met. Some stayed to get to know Him better; others did not. Although their motives for following Him may have been misguided, Jesus did not turn them away. After all, we have a deep need to truly know God and to have a loving, trusting relationship with Him.

◆ ◆ ◆ ◆ ◆ ◆ ◆ ◆ ◆

1. How has your life become more fulfilled by following Jesus?

_____

_____

2. How would you answer someone who says, "I think God accepts me; I'm basically a good person. Besides, nobody's perfect!"

_____

_____

———◆ Faith at Work ◆———

God is intimately interested in your work. He doesn't want you to worship Him on Sunday, then disconnect your faith from the "real world" Monday through Friday. Your work matters to God just as much as your worship does. In fact, if your work is done unto Him, it can become an integral part of worshiping God.

In chapter 3, we discovered that work is not God's curse on the world as a result of Adam's and Eve's sin. Far from it! The Bible calls work a gift from God (Eccl. 3:13; 5:18–19). Granted, many people have misused God's good gift. Some people have developed poor attitudes toward their work, causing them to put forth inferior efforts.

On the other hand, many people become obsessed with their work, turning themselves into workaholics. This behavior costs them their relationships with their families and God.

Where is the balance? Much of it lies in understanding for whom and for what you are working. When you know that Jesus is your "Ultimate Boss," you want to do your best. And Jesus is not unreasonable in His work demands. He knows that you need time for rest, relaxation, and spiritual refreshment. You are encouraged to take the opportunity to improve your personal relationships with your family, friends, and—most of all—God.

◆ ◆ ◆ ◆ ◆ ◆ ◆ ◆ ◆

1. How has understanding that God does not intend your work to be drudgery helped to improve your attitude toward what you do in your workplace?

_____

_____

2. How are you attempting to honor God in your workplace?

_____

_____

3. What are you doing to help keep your work in its proper place in your life?

_____

_____

——◆ Your Family Album ◆——

Maybe you were surprised to learn in chapter 4 that Jesus had some unusual characters in His family tree. But Jesus never denied His roots, and neither should you. You can be thankful for the heritage God has given you. It's part of what makes you who you are, and when you accept and explore your roots, you can develop a better understanding of who you are and how God worked in your family.

When people from different backgrounds are brought together, they have a unique opportunity to demonstrate God's desire for us to accept each other—including our differences—as we are.

◆ ◆ ◆ ◆ ◆ ◆ ◆ ◆ ◆

1. What are you doing in your life that might affirm or show appreciation for your heritage?

_____

_____

_____

2. How has your faith been challenged by knowing that God has used all kinds of people to spread His Word?

_____

_____

_____

——◆ Healing that Hurts ◆——

Loren Cunningham is the founder of Youth with a Mission, an organization that has taken the gospel to every nation on earth. Loren often says, "I believe each of us is either a missionary or a mission field. We are either part of God's answer or part of His problem." Loren deplores believers' lack of loving concern for the lost and hopeless people of the world. "Do you want to allow literally billions of people to die in emptiness and despair, and to step into eternity without knowing Christ?" he asks. "Then do nothing to help these people, and their fate will be sealed."

As we found in chapter 5, Jesus has called us to come out of our safe, comfortable "cocoons" and to become agents of healing among a world of hurting people. Some of those hurting people live across the ocean; some live across the street. In either case, Jesus loves them as much as He loves you. Now, He calls you to take His message of love, hope, and salvation to your world.

◆ ◆ ◆ ◆ ◆ ◆ ◆ ◆ ◆ ◆

1. How is God helping you cope with a painful or difficult situation in your life?

_____

_____

2. What are you doing to reach out to hurting people?

_____

_____

_____

——◆ Clear Commitment ◆——

A man and a woman stand in front of family and friends, and with a few puffs of air a few words are spoken and their lives are never the same. She says, "I do." He says, "I do." Nothing out of the ordinary seems to occur, yet something extremely significant transpires. The couple makes a commitment to each other—a commitment of more than their bodies and emotions. They make a commitment of their wills.

Like marriage, being a believer requires a commitment of your soul to Jesus Christ, and in turn Jesus commits Himself to you: "But as many as received Him, to them He gave the right to become children of God, to those who believe in His name" (John 1:12).

In chapter 6, we discovered that a key test of our commitment to Christ is our love for others. This love is expressed through our attitudes and actions, as well as through our words. God wants us to live openhandedly, always being ready to help others. He wants us to discover the joy of giving generously and blessing others as He has blessed us.

◆ ◆ ◆ ◆ ◆ ◆ ◆ ◆ ◆

1. Why is it so important that you stay in fellowship with other believers?

_____

_____

_____

_____

2. How are you showing Christ's love toward others?

_____

_____

_____

_____

——◆ Turn Away from Temptation ◆——

In chapter 7, we discovered four important facts about temptation and sin:
1. You will be tempted. It is not a question of if temptation will strike your life; the only questions are when and how it will come.
2. It is not a sin to be tempted. Even Jesus was tempted. You only sin if you yield to the temptation.
3. Any time you are tempted, God will provide a way to escape.
4. If you do sin, you can find forgiveness. Confess your sin, repent, and ask God to forgive you and give you His strength to resist future temptations.

When you allow Jesus to work in and through your life, it is possible to endure temptation without giving in to sin. It is when you are at your weakest point that God gives you strength to overcome temptation. All you have to do is ask.

1. How have you learned to pay attention to temptation and to overcome it?

_____

_____

_____

2. Why is it sometimes easier to ask forgiveness from God and from others than it is to forgive ourselves?

_____

_____

_____

3. How has God been able to use your weaknesses to strengthen you?

_____

_____

_____

◆ Keeping the Big Picture ◆

It is easy to start a new project, such as painting a room, writing a book, or starting a new exercise regime. It is another thing to stay on course and complete that project. Some quick starters become discouraged when they find they cannot attain instant gratification. Others do not consider what it will cost them in time, effort, and commitment before they jump into something new.

Jesus frowns upon such fickleness. That's why we examined the cost of following Jesus in chapter 8, as well as the incomparable value of being part of His kingdom and the consequences of turning away from a Christian lifestyle. There is no question about it—being a believer has never been easy, and it is still difficult today. Sometimes you may feel as though you were swimming against the tide, being swept along by problems over which you have no control.

Nevertheless, it is possible for your life to be constantly refilled with God's presence. He will give you the strength you need to keep on track. Scripture tells us to, "trust in the LORD with all your heart, and lean not on your own understanding; in all your ways, acknowledge Him, and He shall direct your paths" (Proverbs 3:5–6). The only safe and secure life is one that is continually filled with the love and power of Christ.

1. Have you ever been tempted to turn your back on Jesus and return to your previous lifestyle? What helps you continue following Jesus?

_____

_____

_____

2. List several sacrifices you have had to make to follow Jesus.

_____

_____

3. How do you know that making these sacrifices will be "worth it" in the long run?

_____

_____

——◆ Show and Tell ◆——

Throughout this workbook, you have been discovering ways to make God's Word relevant to your daily life. As you learn how to live out God's principles, you automatically become a witness to nonbelievers. Nevertheless, it is not always enough simply to live a Christian lifestyle and hope that people notice. Sooner or later, you will need to open your mouth and speak to others about Jesus.

In chapter 9, we looked at some basic ways you can tell your friends, family members, and coworkers Jesus' message. We discovered how Jesus connected with people on their level, and how He focused on the issues that were important to His audience.

Although Jesus commands us to be His witnesses, the Bible also makes it clear that the ultimate success or failure of your efforts is not your responsibility alone. It is up to God to draw a person to Jesus by the power of the Holy Spirit. This knowledge can help you to be more comfortable in speaking to others about Jesus because you understand that your job is to be a faithful witness; the rest is up to Him.

◆ ◆ ◆ ◆ ◆ ◆ ◆ ◆ ◆

1. Why is it so important that what you say about Jesus and the Christian life is consistent with your lifestyle?

_____

_____

2. How have you learned to communicate the gospel to unbelievers?

_____

_____

———◆ New Wine, New Wineskins ◆———

For some people, the words I'm sorry *are some of the hardest words they will ever say. After all, it's hard to admit we have made a mistake. God wants us to regret our sins, but being sorry for our sins is only the first step toward being free from them. True repentance demands a complete turning away from sin—not only a change of heart and mind, but also a change in direction.*

In chapter 10, we explored what it means to allow Christ to change our lives, including our thinking and our behavior. We examined one of the most radical transformation experiences in history—that of Saul, the persecutor of Christians, into Paul, one of Christianity's most powerful proponents. Jesus changes us from the inside out by changing our hearts and our attitudes. At times, some of the changes He brings to our lives may be distressing. But remember, Christ always changes our lives for the better.

◆ ◆ ◆ ◆ ◆ ◆ ◆ ◆ ◆

1. What does it mean to repent of your sins?

_____

_____

_____

2. How is Jesus transforming your life?

_____

_____

_____

———◆ The Serving Spirit ◆———

As you allow God to change you, you develop a new desire to serve others as Jesus did. You start looking for new ways to give to others. Humility begins to take the place once held by pride.

When you sense yourself developing a servant's heart, you will realize how strong your relationship with Christ is. Why? Because such self-effacing service and giving do not come naturally to most human beings. Most of us are too busy looking out for Number One to notice opportunities to serve others.

In chapter 11, we also discovered that we need to develop an attitude of humility to truly serve others. If we don't, then our service will be tainted with selfish motives. Humility is not an option if we want to walk with God—it's a necessity.

✦ ✦ ✦ ✦ ✦ ✦ ✦ ✦ ✦

1. Why are selfishness and servanthood opposite qualities?

_____

_____

_____

2. What is the difference between serving someone you love and serving someone you dislike?

_____

_____

_____

✦ Encouraging Leaders ✦

Throughout history, God has delighted in choosing the most unlikely characters to represent Him. Moses, for instance, readily admitted that he was not a powerful or eloquent public speaker. Yet, God chose Moses to lead His people out of Egypt. The prophet Jeremiah often reminded God that he had nothing to offer Him. God, however, knew that Jeremiah had much to give.

Even Jesus' disciples were lacking in leadership skills. Most of the early believers were poor, uneducated, and probably rather nondescript. They were not trained counselors, nor were they social strategists or professional politicians. They were, however, committed to Jesus. They had learned to trust Him with their lives; as a result, the early believers turned the known world upside down by spreading the gospel.

Today, God continues to develop a new breed of leaders. They are servant-leaders who, instead of seeking power, perks, and self-promotion, are trying to lead by serving their followers. All believers have a responsibility to pray for their leaders and to encourage them whenever possible. Together, as we experience more of God's Word in our lives, we can present an eternal reflection of Christ to the world around us.

1. Why do you think God chooses unlikely people to be used for His work?

_____

_____

2. List three important principles of leadership you have learned, or have been reminded of, as a result of this study.

_____

_____

_____

—◆ What It Means To Be Like Jesus ◆—

Jesus' statement in Matthew 10:25 implies that His disciples will be like Him. To His first-century followers, that included the prospect of persecution and martyrdom. But what else does it mean to "be like Jesus," especially for Christians in today's world?

Matthew 10:25

²⁵It is enough for a disciple that he be like his teacher, and a servant like his master. If they have called the master of the house Beelzebub, how much more *will they call* those of his household!

Eight portraits of Jesus in Matthew's eyewitness account give us some clues. We examined each portrait in chapters 4 through 7 and 9 through 12 of this workbook.

As you prepare to take what you have learned into your world, consider one more time what it means to follow Christ's example of experiencing God's Word in daily life.

EIGHT PORTRAITS OF JESUS
1. To be like Jesus means to accept our roots (1:1–17).
2. To be like Jesus means to engage the world's pain and struggle (1:18—2:23).
3. To be like Jesus means to commit ourselves to other believers, no matter how "weird" they appear to be (3:1–17).
4. To be like Jesus means to admit our vulnerability to temptation (4:1–11).
5. To be like Jesus means to openly proclaim the message of Christ (4:12–25).
6. To be like Jesus means to commit ourselves to changed thinking and behavior (5:1—7:27).
7. To be like Jesus means to serve others, especially those who are oppressed or without Christ (8:1—9:38).
8. To be like Jesus means to affirm others in leadership (10:1–42).

LEADER'S GUIDE TO
EXPERIENCING THE WORD IN YOUR LIFE

This workbook has been prepared primarily for individual study. Nevertheless, it lends itself quite easily to group study and discussion. Because of the personal nature of many of the questions, it is recommended that each member of your group has a workbook to ensure privacy.

You don't need to be a Bible scholar or a motivational speaker to lead a study group. All you need to do is follow the format established in each chapter. The material included in this Leader's Guide is intended to be a supplement for each lesson, not a substitute.

Here are a few suggestions for forming and leading a study group:

1. Your group may be composed of men and women of varying ages. It may be an existing Bible study group, a Sunday school class, or a lunchtime gathering in your workplace. Ideally, the group should not be larger than twelve people. The larger the group is, the more difficult it will be for you to "direct traffic" and keep the discussion focused on the subject.

2. Assign the first chapter to your group and explain that you will be discussing only one chapter each week for the next twelve weeks. Encourage group members to read each article carefully, and answer all questions as thoroughly as possible before coming to class. If there are words, concepts, or Scripture passages a group member does not understand, that person should make note of that in the workbook. These subjects can be addressed during group discussions.

3. Your job as the leader is not to be the "answer person." Your role is to facilitate the discussions. When you introduce the session, be sure to point out that for many of the questions there are no right or wrong answers.

4. Open each class by welcoming everyone. Be sure to greet new members of the group. You may want to share any stories of events from the previous week. If desired, you can open the session with a prayer.

5. Next, you could do a brief review of the previous session. For the first class you may want to begin with the introduction to this workbook. Next you will want to introduce the new lesson. This would be the time to present the objectives for the session. You may want to list them on a chalkboard.

6. One way to begin the discussion is by reading one of the stories or an article in the chapter. The questions listed in this Leader's Guide address the main points of the chapter. If the group wants to focus on a particular issue, feel free to review the relevant articles, Scripture, and questions in more detail. The key to having a successful discussion is getting the group involved; it is not critical to try to work through every question listed. Encourage

personal testimonies of how God is using the members of your group in the workplace, but limit the testimony time to three minutes.

7. In some lessons, it may be helpful to read aloud portions of an article, but be sensitive to those members of your group who may be embarrassed about reading in front of other people. If you have any reason to think someone would feel awkward, read the material aloud yourself.

Also, be aware of anyone who is not taking an active role in the group. If someone is not participating, give that person an opportunity to contribute by saying, "Bob, would you like to share your answer to question two?" If that person appears nervous or uncomfortable answering in front of the group, do not push for an answer. Some people do not like to speak in front of a group. On the other hand, you may have a person who jumps to answer every question, not giving the others a chance to participate. One way to handle this is to say, "That's a good point. Anyone else?"

8. If you complete the questions in the Leader's Guide before the session is over, you can focus on the more specific questions in the chapter. Perhaps a point was made earlier in the session that warrants further discussion. If you come to a question that does not spark much discussion, move on.

9. Some individuals may have specific questions from when they worked through the chapter prior to the session. Encourage everyone to bring up specific questions during the discussion time.

10. At the end of each session, ask the group members to study the next chapter on their own before the next session. Encourage members to pray specifically for each other during the upcoming week. Close the session with a brief prayer of thanksgiving or another appropriate prayer.

11. For a fifty-minute session, allow seven minutes for the welcome and warm-up. Take three minutes to review the previous session. Introduce the new lesson in five minutes. Allow thirty minutes for discussion of this week's chapter, and leave five minutes for closing discussion.

Chapter 1: Getting the Big Picture

Being a Christian does not mean we should only worship God when we are in church. Nor does it mean hiding our heads in the sand when we leave church. God calls us to love Him with our whole hearts, and then share His love with the whole world.

God has given us the Bible and the gospel message of Jesus so that we can have life. We are called to share this message with others. As we learn to follow God's Word more closely, the people around us will notice. In fact, people will be watching us to see how Christians handle responsibilities and resources.

Lesson Objectives

1. To show that being a Christian involves more than token attendance at church services.
2. To examine how Jesus was both a leader and a servant.
3. To get a clear understanding of what the gospel is and why this message must be an integral part of our lives.

4. *To show that Jesus wants the gospel to be presented to the entire world.*
5. *To understand that the Bible is the one standard by which all other truths must be measured because it is the inspired Word of God.*

Discuss

1. How can we love God with *all* our being, like He commands, instead of reserving only one hour a week to worship Him? (See "Life—The Big Picture" on pages 2–3.)
2. Why do you think Jesus emphasized that the gospel is especially good news for the poor (Luke 7:22, page 7)? How can you incorporate the gospel in your daily life?
3. What would you say to someone who asked you, "How do you know you can trust the Bible? Isn't it full of errors and contradictions?" (See "The Bible: Getting the Big Picture" on pages 8–9.)
4. How can your faith make a difference in the world? (See "Faith Impacts the World" on page 11.)

Chapter 2: Unfolding Faith

Some people assume that once they have trusted Christ as their Savior, they have secured their place in heaven. Therefore, they can get on with their lives here on earth. But that is not the case.

Being a Christian and living a Christian lifestyle require growth and maturation, which take time. Jesus calls you to follow Him for the long haul and to put His principles to work in your life on a daily basis.

Nobody is "good enough" to get into God's kingdom on individual merit. When you have faith and trust in Christ, you will experience a peace in your heart and mind that the world can never provide.

Lesson Objectives

1. *To understand that God allows time for our faith to grow.*
2. *To show that it really is worth it to follow Jesus.*
3. *To discover that there is a difference between knowing about God and really knowing Him and having a relationship with God.*
4. *To show that although people are not "good enough" on their own merit, Jesus will make them good if they trust Him.*

Discuss

1. It has been said that religion is man's search for God, but Christianity is God's search for man. What do you think that means?
2. Why do you think Jesus spoke to the crowds in parables? (See "Faith Unfolds Slowly" on page 15.)

3. If someone were to ask you, "What will I get out of following Jesus?" how would you respond? According to Ephesians 1:7 (page 18), what two gifts are now yours because Jesus was crucified?
4. What disciplines have you (or will you) establish to help make your faith a vital part of your life? (Review "Knowing About God Is Not the Same as Knowing God" on pages 19–20.)
5. Is there such a thing as a little sin and a big sin? According to Romans 3:21–26 (page 24), how can we be redeemed?

Chapter 3: Faith at Work

Living out a relationship with Christ in the workplace is not always as easy as it sounds. First we must learn to see work from God's perspective. He expects us to honor Him by doing excellent work and by maintaining a reputation for integrity, fairness, and honesty in all that we do. As Christians, we should approach our work each day as though we were working for God.

Many people have the mistaken notion that we must prove ourselves through our work. But God does not want us to become workaholics; He wants us to enjoy times of rest, relaxation, and spiritual refreshment.

Lesson Objectives

1. *To show that work is not a curse; work is a gift from God.*
2. *To show that God Himself is a worker and that He is extremely interested in our work.*
3. *To understand that believers must take their faith with them into the workplace.*
4. *To realize that our self-worth does not depend on our work. We have value because God created us.*
5. *To learn that we need time to rest and restore our relationships with our families, friends, and God.*

Discuss

1. In 1 Corinthians 3:9 (page 30), Paul refers to us as "God's fellow workers." What do you suppose Paul meant?
2. If work is a gift from God, what are some ways you can express thanks to Him? (See "Is Work a Curse?" on page 32.)
3. Why should believers strive to be the best workers in the workplace?
4. In Colossians 3:22 (page 36), Paul instructs believers to obey their master. How does this apply to your relationship with your boss? Who are you really working for?
5. Does the faith you celebrate on Sunday sometimes feel disconnected from the "real world" you face on Monday? How can you improve the connections between your faith community and the demands of your world? (See "Reconnecting Sundays and Mondays" on pages 39–40.)

Chapter 4: Your Family Album

For most of us, there are some unusual, even embarrassing, characters in our families' backgrounds. But that's okay—even Jesus had such characters in His family. Jesus was never ashamed of His roots, nor did He ever degrade anyone else's family background. He acknowledged the sinners in His lineage, and He accepted the fact that God could bring about good in any situation.

The history of our families is important to each of us. It may be difficult to accept our varying backgrounds, but God values all the people of the world. In fact, God calls us to overcome barriers of race, ethnicity, language, and culture. He wants us to reach out to the world with the truth of the gospel.

Lesson Objectives

1. *To show that although Jesus was a descendant from the royal lineage of King David, His family tree was quite diverse.*
2. *To understand that Jesus is the Messiah for all people, including people whose families have a tainted past.*
3. *To discover that our varied heritages are gifts from God.*
4. *To understand how Paul accepted the good things about his heritage, while rejecting those things in his heritage that contradicted a Christian lifestyle.*

Discuss

1. How far back can you trace your family tree? What are you most proud of about your roots? What embarrasses you about your roots?
2. How has your heritage influenced your lifestyle? Why did Paul view his Jewish background as rubbish on one hand, but a valuable gift from God on the other? (See "Paul the Jew—Teacher of the Gentiles" on page 46.)
3. Review the article "Researching Your Own Religious Roots" on pages 48–49. What role has religion played in your family? What beliefs and practices among your religious roots would you disagree with? Why?

Chapter 5: Healing that Hurts

It is difficult to fully understand the suffering of others unless we experience it ourselves. We tend to insulate ourselves from the world, and God recognizes this tendency to withdraw. That's why He sent Jesus to show us what it means to reach out to the hurting people of this world.

Often the pain a hurting person experiences is more than a physical ailment. It is a deep-seated sense of rejection and of being unimportant. Sometimes just knowing that someone else cares may be all the healing a person needs. Regardless of a person's physical needs, everyone needs to know about the One who can heal not only the body, but also the soul.

We really have only two alternatives when it comes to dealing with hurting people: We can close our eyes and pretend the problems do not exist, or we can obey Jesus and reach out to those in pain.

Lesson Objectives

1. To discover that Jesus' birth was surrounded by stress, awkwardness, and pain. Jesus understands what it feels like to be born into difficult circumstances.
2. To learn how to come out of our "cocoons" and represent Jesus to hurting people all around us.
3. To understand that all pain is not physical; sometimes it is a person's soul that hurts. We can help with both kinds of pain.
4. To learn how God puts a limit on the amount of pain we suffer.

Discuss

1. Many people wonder why a good, loving, all-powerful God allows evil things to happen to good people. Where do you suppose pain, suffering, and evil originate? Why does God allow bad things to happen to good people?
2. Review Matthew 1:18—2:23 on pages 55–56. What key point did Herod misinterpret about Jesus' kingdom? How do many people make that same mistake today?
3. Hebrews 4:16 (page 58) challenges believers to "come boldly to the throne of grace." Why? What does this mean for your life?
4. Some pain is realized over a period of time. This was the case with the hemorrhaging woman Jesus healed in Matthew 9:20–22 (page 60). How did Jesus heal this woman? How can you respond to the needs of the "untouchables" in your community?
5. Review the article "God Restrains Evil" on pages 62–63. How does God place limits on the amount of pain we suffer? Why is it important that we experience some pain in our lives?

Chapter 6: Clear Commitment

Commitment to Christ impacts every area of our lives. It involves our relationships with family, friends, and coworkers. It involves what we do with our time, money, and other resources. And Jesus has called us to commit ourselves to following Him and learning from Him.

We are told that the world will recognize that we belong to God not only by our words, but also by our love for others. And love requires commitment. Without commitment, Christlike love is impossible.

Making a commitment today can be scary, especially as our society becomes more transient. It is difficult to invest ourselves in others, but this is what we must do. Remember that Jesus will be guiding us as we make the effort to commit ourselves to others.

Lesson Objectives

1. To discover how Jesus committed Himself to others. John the Baptist is used as an example.
2. To emphasize that love is the one true sign of a committed believer.

3. *To understand that we have value because of whose we are, not who we are.*
4. *To see how tough times often bring a diverse group of people together to work for a common goal.*

Discuss

1. Jesus commands us to love others as He loved us (see John 13:31–35 on pages 67–68). Shortly after He told His disciples this, Jesus laid down His life for us. How can we demonstrate that kind of love for others?
2. Our modern culture tears at our sense of identity and security. If we want to commit ourselves to others, then we need to know whose we are and why. Do you? Why is this important? (See "God's Family Album" on page 70.)
3. Although the Galilean women who followed Jesus did not do much for Christ, they did what they could (see Luke 23:50–56 and "A Remarkable Coalition" on pages 72–73). How did they show their commitment to Christ? What does this tell you about your commitment to Him?
4. Generosity is not always measurable in dollars and cents. What are some other standards by which you can measure generosity? (See "Sharing Things in Common" on pages 74–75.)

Chapter 7: Turn Away from Temptation

Temptation touches all of us. But being tempted is not the same as sinning. We do not sin until we yield to the temptation. We cannot avoid the initial tempting thoughts that pop into our minds; we can, however, prevent ourselves from dwelling on these thoughts.

Even Jesus was tempted! The difference between Jesus and us is that He did not yield to temptation. That is comforting because Christ showed us that it is possible to defeat temptation.

Keep in mind, though, that none of us is strong enough all the time. Sometimes we are tempted to give up, which usually occurs in a moment of weakness. But, during our times of weakness are when Jesus is strong. He will give us His strength to overcome temptation if we let Him. All we have to do is ask.

Lesson Objectives

1. *To recognize that everyone will be tempted, but temptation itself is not sin.*
2. *To discover that the best way to defeat temptation is to acknowledge its existence in our lives, recognize our vulnerability, and be willing to let Jesus help us.*
3. *To see how Jesus overcame temptation by using the Word of God against Satan.*
4. *To discover that God will never allow us to be tempted more than we can bear, and with every temptation He will provide a way to escape.*
5. *To reassure believers that if we do fail, forgiveness is available if we genuinely repent and turn away from sin.*

Discuss

1. What alternatives to temptation does Scripture offer? (See "Pay Attention to Temptation!" on pages 82–83.)
2. What are the roots of sin? (See "The Roots of Sin" and James 1:13–18 on pages 84–85.) How can you overcome temptation?
3. When you receive an enticing offer that promises you everything you want, do you consider the benefits of the offer or the cost? (See "All Will be Yours" on page 85.)
4. Satan often tempts by saying, "You've been so good lately. God wouldn't blame you if you took a little time off." Why can't you afford to take a little time off?
5. In Luke 22:39–46 (page 88), Jesus warned His disciples twice to pray so they would not enter into temptation. Why did He say that?
6. How has God used your weaknesses to strengthen you? (See "When I Am Weak, Then I Am Strong" on page 89.)

Chapter 8: Keeping the Big Picture

Sometimes we become discouraged as we strive to become more like Jesus, especially when things are not going our way. We have to keep in mind that living for Him is worth any price.

Beginning the journey of faith is exciting, but we need to be careful about giving up on the journey. We must persevere, which can be hard to do—especially when everything in us wants to quit. We reason, Look how far we've already come!

Jesus frowns on such fickleness. Being a Christian is not easy. Sometimes we may feel like we are swimming against the tide, barely able to stay afloat. But God will not leave us to drown. He is there to guide and support us as long as we let Him.

Lesson Objectives

1. *To encourage believers to continue following Christ, regardless of the sacrifice or cost involved.*
2. *To understand that we need to continually renew our faith and our spiritual lives.*
3. *To remind believers that it is not enough to start well in our journey with Jesus; we must finish well, too.*

Discuss

1. What steps can you take to continue growing in your spiritual life, thus preventing you from falling away? (See "Turning Back Is Awful" on pages 95–96.)
2. What has your commitment to Christ cost you? Has it made any difference in decisions you have made about your career, lifestyle, or investments? (See "The Incomparable Value of the Kingdom" on page 97.)
3. Where do you go for spiritual renewal? If you don't have such a place, how can you find one? (See "Being Renewed and Renewed" on page 99.)

4. How does Peter affirm the value of the here and now, as well as the value of the future (2 Peter 3:8–18, page 103)? What decisions or events have had the most impact on your life so far?

Chapter 9: Show and Tell

Jesus has called us to be fishers of men, and He has filled us with the power of the Holy Spirit so we can do this. Yet, many believers are reluctant to tell others about Jesus. They may fear being rejected or making a mistake. Some believers hope that people will simply notice the difference Christ has made in their lives.

But Jesus has called us to proclaim His message to others in addition to living a Christian lifestyle. We must learn to meet people where they are and relate to them in a way that they will understand. Sharing the gospel with others in addition to living a lifestyle that demonstrates this message offer nonbelievers a valid example of what it means to be a Christian.

While Jesus tells us to be His witnesses, He also makes it clear that the ultimate success or failure of your efforts is not your responsibility alone. Unless God draws a person to Jesus by the power of the Holy Spirit, then that person cannot be saved. Your job is to be a faithful witness; the rest is up to God.

Lesson Objectives

1. *To realize that we must put words with our actions if we are going to be effective witnesses for Christ.*
2. *To recognize the need for absolute honesty and integrity in our witnessing.*
3. *To see how Jesus approached various types of people with the gospel. He tailored His message to meet His listeners where they were most comfortable.*
4. *To understand that it is God who brings a person to Christ, not us alone.*

Discuss

1. Why do you think many believers and unbelievers alike have a distaste for witnessing?
2. What exactly does it mean to "witness"? (See "Some Basics of Witness" on page 108.) What does it take for someone to be an effective witness?
3. Paul presented a straightforward message to the Thessalonians (1 Thess. 2:4–12, pages 110–111), which added to his credibility. Are there things about your methods or motives that conflict with the message you are trying to communicate?
4. In Acts 2:37–41 and "Carrots, Not Sticks" (page 112), we learn that it is the Holy Spirit who guides people to God. Why, then, are we called to be witnesses?

Chapter 10: New Wine, New Wineskins

Change is a part of life; each of us changes every day. Often we don't mind the changes, but as soon as we are faced with major changes or changes over which we have no control, then we become resentful.

Trusting Jesus is a major change. He changes our priorities, our thinking, our aspiration, and our understanding of life itself. Jesus alters us from the inside out by changing our hearts and our attitudes, which in turn changes the way we function in the world. At times, some of the changes Jesus brings about in our lives may be disconcerting. But we can be certain of this: He always changes our lives for the better.

Lesson Objectives

1. *To understand the meaning of and the need for repentance, which brings about positive change in our lives.*
2. *To examine the "Sermon on the Mount" as a good place to begin in changing our attitudes and our behavior.*
3. *To learn more about what God's kingdom is and understand the difference it makes in our lives.*
4. *To see how Saul, a persecutor of Christians, met Jesus and made a drastic change in his life, becoming Paul, the missionary and author of much of the New Testament.*

Discuss

1. It is easy to understand why nonbelievers are reluctant to allow Christ to change them. They don't know Jesus. But why do you think Christians are so resistant to the changes Jesus wants to make in their lives?
2. Scan through the "Sermon on the Mount" (pages 116–120) and see how many of the Ten Commandments you can find. What is the significance of this? According to Matthew 7:21–27 (page 120), what is the true test of Christ's transforming power in our lives?
3. What does it mean to repent of your sins? Why is it so important that we make changes in our lives in order to follow Jesus? (See "The King Declares His Kingdom" on pages 122–123.)
4. In Galatians 1:13–17 (page 127), Paul shares part of his testimony of how his encounter with Jesus changed his life. What or whom has God used to get your attention and point your life in a different direction?

Chapter 11: The Serving Spirit

Christ calls us to serve fellow believers, our family members, our communities, and our world, which is not an easy task. This job is especially difficult because putting someone else's needs before our own often goes against our nature.

In order for us to serve others, we must adopt an attitude of humility. If we do not, then our motives will be tainted by selfishness. We would be doing the right thing, but for the wrong reasons. Actually, humility is not an option for believers—it is an essential part of our lives if we want to follow Christ.

Lesson Objectives

1. *To understand why we must serve others, including those we don't like.*
2. *To understand that humility and servitude are compatible qualities.*

3. To recognize the difference between serving others in a risky situation and endangering ourselves by trying to serve in dangerous situations.
4. To see that even Jesus did not come to be served, but to serve us.

Discuss

1. It's relatively easy for us to serve someone we know and like, but we are told we must also serve people we do not like (Matt. 8:1—9:38, pages 132–134). Who are some of the people in your life who are difficult to serve?
2. What is humility and why is it an important part of a believer's lifestyle? (See "Humility—The Scandalous Virtue" on page 136.)
3. What difference does faith make in the way you respond to people in need? (See "Running to Extremes" on pages 138–139.)
4. In John 13:1–20 (page 141), Jesus washed the feet of His disciples—including Judas, who was about to betray Him. What does Christ's willingness to wash Judas' feet say about serving those who betray you?

Chapter 12: Encouraging Leaders

In order to be an effective leader, we must first learn how to follow and serve. Power and authority will eventually become useless in the hands of someone who does not have a servant's heart.

When people lead as Jesus did, the world begins to see genuine leadership. As people see virtuous behavior in their leaders, they respond to the leader in a positive way. People respect a righteous, honest leader who is willing to admit when help is needed. Remember that all leaders need our support. They are human, just like us, and they have their weak or difficult moments, too.

There will be times when we cannot respect certain leaders. It is our responsibility, though, to respect the position that person holds. Keep in mind that God is our ultimate Leader, and He will deal with immoral individuals.

Lesson Objectives

1. To show that Jesus is depending upon us to spread the gospel message.
2. To understand that authority should be handled responsibly, not for personal pleasure or advantage.
3. To see how important it is to be faithful to our leaders by carrying out our responsibilities, even when that leader is not around.
4. To recognize that leaders need our encouragement and positive words.
5. To show that when a decision must be made whether to obey God's authority or man's, the believer must always choose to obey God.

Discuss

1. How does Jesus call us to help others grow? Why is that an important trait of a good leader? (See "What It Means to be Like Jesus" on pages 145–146.)
2. Do you exercise authority over others for your own benefit or for the good of others? What is the difference? (See "Spiritual Authority" and 2 Corinthians 13:9–10 on pages 148–149.)
3. Why is it so awful to know your leader's wishes and not carry them out (Luke 12:47–48, page 150)?
4. How can you encourage your leaders? (See "Encouraging the Boss," page 152.)
5. What should Christians do when faced with a conflict between human authority and God's authority? (See "We Ought to Obey God Rather than Men" and Acts 5:22–32, pages 154–155.)
6. Is it ever right for a leader to lie to his or her followers in order to protect them?